THE
SILENCED

THE
SILENCED

CLAUDIO FAVA

Translated by Sahar Zivan

POLARIS
PUBLISHING

This edition first published in 2021 by

POLARIS PUBLISHING LTD
c/o Aberdein Considine
2nd Floor, Elder House
Multrees Walk
Edinburgh
EH1 3DX

Distributed by
Birlinn Limited

www.polarispublishing.com

Text copyright © Claudio Fava, 2021
Translation copyright © Sahar Zivan, 2021

First published in Italy in 2013 by Add Editore, Torino as *Mar del Plata*

ISBN: 9781913538293
eBook ISBN: 9781913538309

This book has been translated thanks to a grant awarded
by the Italian Ministry of Foreign Affairs and International Cooperation
*Questo libro è stato tradotto grazie a un contributo del Ministero
degli Affari Esteri e della Cooperazione Internazionale italiano.*

British Library Cataloguing-in-Publication Data
A catalogue record for this book is available on request from the British Library.

Designed and typeset by Polaris Publishing, Edinburgh
Printed in Great Britain by MBM Print, East Kilbride

PROLOGUE

Raúl Barandiarán has a name that tells a story of its own. One grandfather is Italian, the other Basque, from a small village near San Sebastián. 'When I go back there I feel like a separatist,' he says with the hint of a smile, or perhaps it's a wry grin, 'and I feel loved.'

Raúl is the sole survivor of the original Club La Plata 1st XV of 1975, an Argentine rugby team. Over the course of four years, twenty of his teammates were murdered: gunned down, assassinated, 'disappeared', in an attempt to tear a generation – and an entire squad – out by its roots, leaving them with no way to rebuild. But Raúl lived. Part Italian, part Basque, part survivor.

The smile finally stretches further across his face, his distinctive jaw line crossed with faint scars – heirlooms from years spent on the rugby field. On one occasion, a stray elbow resulted in part of his tongue being sliced off: it was reattached with needle and thread, and two weeks later he was back out on the pitch.

Raúl was always a difficult man to keep down, even during the horrific years of Jorge Rafael Videla's dictatorship, when the president's henchmen brutally slaughtered more than 30,000 Argentines. Among them were Raúl's teammates, brothers on and off the field, *muchachos* who grew up together on the town's rugby pitches. If you ask him to revive the memories, he'll tell you: 'It's bad for me.' Followed by: 'Then again, it's also good. For others. Those whose memories could use a jolt. Those who weren't there. Those who think that 30,000 dead and disappeared are no more than a historical footnote, rather than a piece of raw flesh that was torn to shreds by this country.'

I meet him at his home in La Plata, a few steps from the rugby team's home ground. He shows me match-day pictures of the team – stick-thin, all flowing locks and fierce facial expressions. They were a good group of boys, he tells me.

'The best – we were unbeatable at sevens. But we never got called up to the national side. Rugby is a right-wing sport in Argentina, and we were on the left.'

The left. During the years of the military junta, operatives driving Ford Falcons without number plates would show up to drag 'subversives' from their beds in the middle of the night and take them to be interrogated, tortured and murdered. It didn't take much to be considered a subversive. Belonging to the wrong political group. Speaking out in the wrong way. Holding your silence at the wrong time.

'Like Hernan Rocca, the first one they assassinated. They followed him home from training one night. They stopped him en route and they murdered him right there on the Pan-American Highway. They put nineteen bullets in him.'

Nineteen bullets: one for him, one for each of the other players in the squad.

'Then it was Otilio's turn. His body was found floating in the Río de la Plata, bloated beyond recognition by the water, arms bound tightly, hands chopped off, a bullet in his head.'

Otilio had been thrown out of an aeroplane, a fate that befell thousands of others during those terrible years. They were known as *los desaparecidos*, 'the disappeared', and it was easier for the regime if they stayed that way after death: there were fewer problems if there was no body to mourn over.

Then it was the turn of the others. Mariano, the captain. Santiago. Pablo. For three years the list grew longer and longer. And what did he, Raúl, do?

'I played on. I was part of a small Trotskyite political group, and we decided that it was the right thing for me to do: to keep heading out onto the pitch, to keep pretending nothing was wrong while my friends continued to fall around me.'

Every death opened another wound, a fresh horror, another laceration of his soul. And still Raúl continued to play; it was the only way to rise above it and to keep living. To not let them win. His way of honouring his fallen teammates.

'A long tour to Europe with the team saved my life. For a whole month, I was able to see things from a distance. When I returned, I understood that the fear would have killed me. But rugby teaches you to overcome your fear; otherwise you'd never go near the ball . . .'

Talking about it now, his voice is soft, as if he is narrating a children's fairy-tale. It wasn't like that at the time. Nor afterwards, when Videla's regime collapsed.

'I went through twelve years of therapy after the dictatorship was brought down. It was very little use, nothing more than a cooling balm on my soul. Healing is something else entirely.'

It was love that saved him.

'Her name was Silvia. I was twenty-seven years old. I was in love, I wanted to get married. Besides, my whole body was battered and bruised from playing . . . a shoulder, a knee, my ribs. It felt like I'd been hit by a train.'

His playing career ended. As did the dictatorship. And so too the romance. His career as an architect remained. And so did the memories, still fresh in his mind.

'These days, the club's board are all right-wing – supporters of former President Macri. Whenever a journalist gets in touch to ask about the team's history, they send them to me. "That's why we have Raúl," they say.'

Raúl is there to remember and remind others.

Matter-of-fact and without a trace of melancholy, in the familiar manner of those who bear the survivor's cross; those who are called upon to speak on behalf of those who are no longer able. Occasionally finding strength in a smile, just as they would have wanted it.

1

The skinny boy in the loose-fitting red shirt stretched his arms out, palms upturned as if appealing to the gods. He caught the ball, clutched it tightly to his chest, and set off downfield pursued by a stocky, lumbering brute who tried in vain to grab hold of his shorts, legs, ankles, anything. He was left cursing as the lanky teen slipped between his fingers with a grin erupting across his face. He reached the try line, gave the ball a playful bite and abandoned it on the ground as if it was suddenly of no further value: it was his way of saying he had had his fill.

Another four points to round off a merciless result

with six tries the difference between the teams and the Corrientes boys left to return home with their heads bowed and a lesson learned about how rugby was played in La Plata – how the drop-goals split the sky without wavering, the ball slicing through the air like a dart, how the backline could open your defence with staggering ease, how their wings bolted down the line like trains, like a curse, like a . . .

The clip round the back of the head caught him by surprise.

'*Raúlito!* Wake up!'

The boss had caught up with him in the middle of the pitch, dragging his wounded leg behind him, his hand already raised to deliver the next blow. Raúl instinctively raised his arms to protect his face.

'Stop messing about, there's still five minutes to go!'

'I know . . .'

'You don't know shit! Do you want to watch the next game from the stands?'

Raúl shook his head. He wanted nothing else in

life but to play. The next game and all the ones that would come after it – that was why he'd left home before he'd even turned sixteen – to play rugby every Saturday, every Sunday, every day God gave him. When he looked down at his hands, he found it strange to see them hanging empty – useless – when they should be gripping a rugby ball, spinning out passes, chipping or punting, or raising the ball to his mouth for the celebratory bite that marked every try. They were bites of a life Raúl had not yet begun to fully live. Twenty was an unhappy age; he found himself caught in the middle of too many life-altering decisions when all he really wanted was to be on the pitch with nothing in his mind beyond the faded leather ball.

'Go on, play...' the boss told him, his tone softening a little.

He liked this kid. Raúl Barandiarán Tombolini – a mouthful of a name and a handful on the pitch, all skin and bones but stubborn as a bull when he set his mind to something. His fast feet, long reach and sinewy body would have seen him picked out for fencing or boxing had he grown up elsewhere. But he had been born in San Telmo, the oldest *barrio* in Buenos Aires. There were no gyms in a place like San Telmo, and not a glove in sight – even a sport like boxing was seen as a bourgeois pursuit. No, for the kids of San Telmo there was only a roughly marked out pitch of hard sand and grit, with two sticks to serve as goalposts at either end. In San Telmo you could choose between football and rugby. Raúl had chosen rugby because he liked to use his hands as well as his feet.

When he had first started playing, the 'oldies' on the team – eighteen-year-olds who spent their Saturday evenings drinking Quilmes on the Avenida Costanera that ran the length of the Buenos Aires coast – had taught him to think of the mud-spattered ball as a part of his own flesh, 'A piece of your heart. If an opponent wants to take it from you, he'll have to stab you first. Understand, *nene*?'

Raúl had understood and it had informed the way he grew up: he may have been tall and thin but he was totally uncompromising. He had left school because he was incapable of sitting still behind a desk for any length of time. It made him feel trapped on all sides. Every so often, he would ask for permission to go to the bathroom, and once he was out of the classroom, he would escape the school grounds and go running down the street, elbows tucked in, head tucked low and eyes fixed ahead, all the way to the first row of brightly coloured houses that marked the start of La Boca, then down to the waterside that reeked of petroleum and the fetid stench of stagnant water. There he would stand for a while, observing the weary faces of the prostitutes in their floral print dresses, before turning and running back again, counting his paces, clearing his head of superfluous thoughts, of the sounds of a country he still truly knew nothing of, of the sights of graffiti-spattered walls with increasingly furious slogans: *Perón come back . . . Long live Perón . . . Death to Perón . . .*

*

He had been introduced to the club in La Plata by his PE teacher. 'Forget about school,' his teacher had told him. 'It won't make you rich or clever.' He had seen Raúl playing on the neighbourhood pitch, his shovel-like hands sending opponents spinning into the dirt like skittles. It seemed like a waste for him to pursue a career as a pen-pusher or an accountant – besides, who would entrust their money to a gangly accountant like him?

A relentless drizzle – that Raúl's Sicilian grandfather would nostalgically call *assuppaviddani* – had fallen from a slate grey sky on his first afternoon at the club. *Assuppaviddani*, which in the local Sicilian dialect meant 'a souper', would soak the farmers to the bone, leaving them to quietly decay from the damp, day after day. It was the reason his grandfather had migrated from Sicily to Argentina when he was seventeen. He had worked as a herdsman on the farms that stretched across the vast expanses of Río Negro in northern Patagonia. Here, the grasslands extended all the way to the horizon, and the sky dipped to meet a landscape so flat and unchanging that it could make you feel unsteady on your feet. Sometime later, Raúl's father was born. He too grew up looking after the cows, and he too made his escape at the same age as his father. He jumped on a bus one day and went to find a job in Buenos Aires, or Capital, as the locals simply called it. He found a job as a cobbler down an alley in San Telmo, where there were so many second-generation Italians that there was no real need to learn Spanish.

Raúl was born and brought up in San Telmo, until the afternoon when his PE teacher put him on an Estrella del Este bus and accompanied him down to see the coast – the real kind – down in La Plata. 'The coach is a friend of mine,' his teacher had told him. 'We used to play together back in the day. They might take you on, and they might even pay for your bus fare to go home once a week.'

Raúl had no desire to go back home, but he said nothing – he was too distracted by what he was seeing from the window of the bus, none of which seemed real. The houses disappearing behind him and the ocean shimmered ahead, its waters encroaching wherever it found channels in the landscape, in a shade of blue he had never seen before – intense, flawless, at times perfectly smooth, at other times foaming white and wild. Its vastness, its obvious power, its unknowable depths had all unnerved him, although he had never admitted as much to anyone. He was from a family of stubborn and brave men who seldom showed weakness and never admitted to fear of anyone or anything.

That afternoon on the pitch, they had put a ball in his hands and told him to run.

'Where?'

'Wherever you want. Through the middle, down the line. Just run.'

He had tucked the ball under his arm and set off, head down, shoulders hunched, nothing in front of his eyes except the ground passing under his feet, like the bulls that his father would tell him about that were driven to fury by melancholy or old age; the poor beasts would lose their minds and start charging across the fields, their hooves eating up the ground, and the only thing you could do was to keep your distance because in those moments they couldn't tell friend from foe and no fence, river or cliff could hold them, and the cowherd's voice held no authority over them.

Just like those bulls, Raúl charged down that rugby pitch, eating up the yards towards the try line – until three players combined to bring him down; a pile of bodies with Raúl crushed underneath, while his teacher looked on with a smile.

He was in the 1st XV two weeks later. He won his first championship at the age of eighteen. He used the money he was given to buy a motorbike – an old Guzzi model – and started telling people it was the same one used by Che Guevara himself, *la Poderosa*, the one he had ridden before he left Argentina and set off on his crazy exploits around the world. Nobody believed him, of course, but he didn't care. It served the same purpose as the rugby: it helped him believe that things would always turn out alright. Even for someone like him, the son of a cobbler and the grandson of a cowherd.

2

The changing room was little more than a line of hooks hanging on a wall and was heavy with the pungent odour of muscle liniment that stung the nostrils and cleared the sinuses. Beneath the showerheads, the players of Club La Plata were in a celebratory mood. They were twenty years old and the match and the victory had already been forgotten. Saturday night lay ahead, and despite money being too tight for anything extravagant, their excitement was still building. They would go for a few beers and a platter of *chuleta* – grilled pork chops – down in Puerto Madero at one of the tables facing a waterfront that was neither river nor ocean, just a strip of water that had forgotten its roots and lazed peacefully against the masonry of the port. At least it was cooler there, with a salt-infused breeze that ruddied the skin. Time would pass quickly there, the boys having so much fun that the verbal assaults they had endured from their coach, who had stood in front of the showers, all his weight resting on his good leg, would soon be a distant memory.

'Forget about the title!' he had yelled and spat. 'Play like you did today and you can forget all of it, even what the ball looks like!'

Hugo Passarella had uneven features bisected by thin lips that were always pursed tight. He too had been a rugby player, once upon a time – until his leg had been broken in a league match, and he had been dragging it behind him like a petulant child ever since. 'Get yourself a cane,' his friends had told him. To which he replied: 'No. It would feel like giving in.' An old man with a gammy leg and a frog in his throat, what sort of coach was that? Besides, he knew he'd only end up using the stick to smack some sense into people. Better off without. Better a cripple.

He had recruited his players when they were still young boys and he had taught them how to play rugby one step at a time, spoon-feeding them everything they needed to know, explaining how to keep their elbows high and their chests low in the scrum to gain an edge over the opposing pack, drawing an outline of the pitch on a piece of cardboard and showing each player where they should and should not go and what they should and should not expect, because the ball was an unfaithful partner; it was unreliable, going where it pleased and never doing what it promised. By simply standing there and waiting for it, you were letting it cuckold you! 'And you are not to be cuckolded. You are the Club La Plata first team and this season you have a title to win. Understand, you bastards?'

The bastards in question nodded silently. Good boys, on the whole, with a touch of arrogance about them. Passarella knew that. But if he were to allow them to convince themselves of their own greatness, they would immediately lose focus. That was why he gave them both barrels after every training session. Some of them were students at the university, others were not yet out of school, one worked as a postman, one as a baker, and a few worked in a factory.

Raúl knew his way around tacks, threads and fabrics, and could have become a cobbler like his father. Instead, he had opened a small garage, working as a mechanic when he felt like it and when he wasn't too tired from training. Once a week, if all was well. Residents in the outer barrios tended to use the bus anyway, and the few cars that could be found on the roads in the suburbs were often old and ungainly American models with cardboard in place of the original leather upholstery – and there were no spare parts anyway because it cost too much to import them from the other side of the world. When the cars eventually gave out, they would be abandoned in a parking garage, like an old pair of worn-out shoes on top of a bin.

*

It is 1978, and the military has held power in Argentina for the past two years. They order, threaten and kill. In their own way, they appear to be enjoying themselves. At the moment they are busy making preparations for the upcoming FIFA World Cup, an occasion that will see the eyes of the world focused on the host nation like never before. But was that something for the junta to be concerned about? After all, what do the Italians or the Germans care about the dark and putrid undercurrents sweeping Argentina? Why should the Brazilians or Russians give a damn that Jorge Rafael Videla has proclaimed himself president for life and is busy screwing over the country? What fault is it of the French and the Hungarians if he and his fellow admirals and generals have decided that this is how Argentina is to be managed from here on in: cleaned up at the point of a bayonet, sweeping away hotheads and revolutionaries, anarchists, paedophiles, scruffy men, men who look like fags, communists, socialists, vagabonds, Peronists, radicals, nuns, trade unionists, prostitutes, students, professors, so-called pacifists, the mentally ill, slackers, heathens . . . what on earth do you expect the government to do, just let them take over the country, filling the heads of our sons and daughters with the nonsense put out by the third-worldists and let them fall into communism? Tell me, what you would have us do? Tell me, honestly, what would you do if you saw them pissing on the homeland, on the flag, the uniform, the cross, on the sacraments . . .

His Excellency Videla and his friends knew all too well what was to be done – he had pronounced his judgment in no uncertain terms on the day he ascended to the throne: first we eliminate the subversive elements, then their friends, and finally those who are undecided. Now, why the long faces?

What on earth do you have to whine about? Think about the celebration, shit, think about the World Cup and our *Albiceleste* holding the trophy aloft, which you can bet they will – and don't worry, betting on such things is neither crime nor sin – betting on our boys, all of them pure of heart and mind, not one of them with long hair, not one of them raised among communists, betting on Argentina to go all the way is an act of patriotism . . .

*

'You need a lift, Mono?'

Sitting on his Guzzi, Raúl paused at the entrance to the ground. Engine running, one hand twisting the accelerator slightly. Otilio was always the last one out of the showers. He was lean and quick, baby-faced and without a wisp of facial hair. They called him *Mono* – monkey – because of the long, gangly arms with which he would propel himself into the air at every lineout. At first glance, he appeared to be a good kid who had wandered into the heart of the pack by accident, but in truth he was as hard-headed as they came and wasn't shy about clearing out rucks, smashing through anything that stood between him and the ball.

'So? You coming or not?'

Mono cast a loving gaze over the Guzzi. Then he cocked his head to the side and examined Raúl.

'You're not going for a beer with the others?' he asked.

No, that evening Raúl was going nowhere. He had promised as much to Teresa. Give me one Saturday, she had pleaded, and how could Raúl say no? While he pretended to be a mechanic, Teresita was the one who brought in the money, working in a greasy spoon in La Boca mornings and evenings, every damn day, because her boss paid her to be there, to wash mugs and make omelettes and *huevos revueltos* from nine o'clock every morning and returning home when it was dark outside. That was how it had started – 'You're letting it take over your life, *Teresita mía*, breathing in fried oil all day for 200 pesos—'

'No, what's taking over my life is the fear of losing this job, otherwise how else will we get by, and how will we support a child? And when will we have a child and become a real family?'

'But we are a real family, Teresita, you and I are a family, you and me and the guys from La Plata. I can't give up on the rugby—'

'Who's asking you to give up on the rugby? I'm just asking you for one Saturday, just *one* Saturday a month. For Christ's sake, Raúl, can you not give up one Saturday a month? We can have a beer at home together and have sex.'

'Saturday evening would be depressing, Teresita. That's when the old people do it.'

'Well, we'll do it too because on Sunday I don't have to set an alarm for seven. So I'll wait for you tonight after the game. I'll be waiting for you Raúl, okay?'

She had given him that unmistakable look, the one she had used when they were still at school, when she would call him Raúlito and stare him down with those bewitching eyes, waiting for him to lower his gaze and concede.

'I'm going home tonight, Mono. Otherwise I might get back to find Teresa gone. Do you want a lift or not?'

Mono was still in school, too young to join his teammates for the post-match beer. He lived with his mother in San Telmo, the barrio where the Italians had first made land a hundred years before and never left. He lived in one of the *conventillos*, a post-colonial, nineteenth-century building comprised of flats that had become part of the landscape over time, as if they had always been there – plaster peeling off the walls, wooden shutters over the windows, rust-covered railings, the bathroom at the end of the hallway and an old mulberry tree in the courtyard. As to how that mulberry tree had made it to San Telmo,

Otilio had long since stopped asking himself: it was there and that was enough for the families living in the building. They would defend that tree with more fervour than they would themselves, more than they would their country, their homeland. You could take it all but not that mulberry; the mulberry is ours, it has lived alongside us throughout all these years, keeping us cool in the summer with its dense foliage overhead and giving us a festive feeling over Christmas with the baubles hanging off it – not to mention that it offers a view worthy of the name. Without it, all we would see from our windows would be other windows, other conventillos awkwardly divided up by Perón's surveyors with the residents all partners in the same sad existence and experiencing the same constant longing for something more. At least with Perón there had been someone there – on Sundays he would address the people from the balcony of the Casa Rosada, and you would wear your Sunday best and go and hear him and when you returned you would feel as if you had done something worthwhile, been on a journey. Now all that remained were those old houses with the rusty railings and the shutters with the faded colours. And the mulberry. And Otilio, the monkey who had grown up alright in that home.

'In which case, Raúlito, take me home!'

'You call that dump you live in a home?'

'And you call this wreck a motorbike?'

Raúl leaned over and gripped Mono's ear between his thumb and forefinger. 'Climb on, dumbass. It's getting late.'

Late for what, Mono wondered. Where he lived there was only his mother, who had raised him alone from birth. He hauled himself onto the back of the Guzzi and because Raúl was on the accelerator, he held on firmly to the steel chassis. He had already found himself sitting in mid-air once before when Raúl had twisted the throttle like it was a Japanese racing bike and left him behind. He had fallen on his arse and immediately jumped back up, but Raúl had told everyone about it in the showers after their next match and Mono hadn't been allowed to forget it for the rest of the season. It was hard to believe that it had been only a year earlier – to Otilio it seemed like another lifetime. Every so often he felt as though he had finally managed to get a grip on time, to grab it by the ankles and bring it to ground, but he was always too late. Everything had always happened already.

'Do you think we'll win the championship?'

'You heard the boss. We're not winning shit this year.'

'And you believe him?'

'No.'

And he didn't. It was just how the boss was – negative, quick to anger, with a dark streak inside and out. Raúl loved him like a father, but he had never seen him laugh. Of course they would win the championship again. They always did. And that was as it should be – they were the strongest and the toughest.

'We're here, *hermano* . . .'

Raúl pulled over and left the Guzzi idling, the four-stroke engine drumming its marching tune.

'Maybe if we do win, we'll be invited to go and play in Italy,' said Mono.

'What would we do in Italy?'

'I've heard they play rugby there in stadiums the size of Boca's. We'll win the championship and get ourselves invited to a tournament there. What do you say, Raúlito?'

'Think about your exams, that's what I say. They're less than two months away.'

Raúl kicked the Guzzi into gear and rode off.

He left without turning his head – and if he had he might have noticed the black Ford Falcon parked across the street. He might also have noticed the two men sitting inside who were stepping out and making their way quickly to the open door to Mono's building, now just three paces behind him. One of them was thin as a rake and stooped like an oversized apostrophe, while the other was smaller and appeared nervous, taking long strides like a boxer heading into the ring.

Otilio failed to notice them too. He climbed the stairs, the bag with his damp and muddy kit slung over one shoulder.

'Mum!' he called out, still two floors below, '. . . we destroyed them . . . Mum!'

There was no answer. The door was slightly ajar. Otilio pushed it open and froze. His mother was standing in front of him, stiff and upright, an expression on her face that he had never seen before.

'Mum? What's . . .'

The question hung unfinished in the air. Two silhouettes stepped out from the darkness in the room and shoved Otilio into the wall, pressing his head into the plaster and placing a muzzle against his cheek. He heard footsteps coming up the stairwell.

'Is this him?' a voice asked. It had a rasping, clipped tone.

'Let's ask him now . . .' replied one of the others.

Otilio could feel his breath on his ear.

'Otilio Pascua, right?'

He didn't reply. The man brought his face closer, his voice dropping to a whisper.

'Senior year at Liceo Bolívar . . . That's you, right . . . Mono?'

The boy tipped his head in acknowledgement.

A scream sliced through the darkness behind him. Otilio turned and saw his mother held fast between two of the assailants. One of them silenced her with an open hand across the face: that cry – the primal howl of a wounded animal – had come from her. Otilio tried to say something, but no sooner had he opened his mouth than a burlap sack was placed over his head and tightened. And then everything faded to black.

3

Two days later, the boys were all back at training. Raúl, Pablo, Jorge, Gustavo, Santiago, *El Turco*, Mariano . . . the boss had sent them to run laps because he could still sense their hangovers. They had blurred vision and were short of breath after two laps of the pitch. 'Hurry up, you bastards. Quicker!'

Running ahead of the others because he couldn't stand to be left behind was Pablo, a postman by trade. During the day he racked up the miles on his bike, delivering mail around the houses of Recoleta, before showing up at the club and running the length of the pitch, back and forth, with opponents left trailing in his wake and never coming close to landing a finger on him.

Running behind him was El Turco, the old man of the team at thirty years old. Short and squat, he worked as a tanner during the day – soaking, splitting, tanning, drying and stitching hides – giving him the physical appearance of an innkeeper from the Middle Ages. As one of nature's natural-born props, training wasn't really his forte – it was on the pitch that he came to life, shoving opposing scrums backwards and protecting the ball like it was the mother he'd never met.

Also running was Jorge, the twenty-year-old second row who was built like a wardrobe and who had aspirations of becoming a doctor. Then there was Mariano, who worked in a pottery and had hands like shovels. Next to him was Santiago, with his frizzy hair and raven-black eyes that hinted at indigenous heritage, although nobody knew with any certainty where he was from or even what he did for a living – all they knew was that when he was flying downfield with the ball clutched to his chest like a new-born baby, it looked like he was hovering above the rough surface, oblivious to the divots and ruts that had been cut up by a thousand boots and which slowed everyone else down. Gustavo – the youngest member of the team at only sixteen– was light as a feather but with the agility of a hare; he was the regular lineout jumper, always climbing highest to retrieve the muddy ball, the raised hands of the others doing little more than saluting it before he clutched it for his team.

Running with them was Raúl, free from the hangover afflicting his teammates after Teresa had kept him all to herself that weekend – Saturday and Sunday night, with fleeting discussions about love and children.

'What children, Teresa?' Raúl had asked.

'Children, Raúlito, children! Were you never a child yourself?'

'I'm still young, Teresa.'

'You're turning twenty-one in two months – you're old, ancient. Now, let's go. Take me out for lunch.'

It was Sunday morning, it had rained all night, and the air was clear and fresh.

'Let's go to the beach.'

So they'd gone to one of the shacks where they fried fish and sold it in cones for two pesos each and Teresa had been truly happy and Raúl was happy too, although he was missing something – the game, the boss, the boys – but he hadn't let on. 'I'm happy too,' he had told Teresa, 'but now let's go home and make love because after we have children we won't be able to anymore. Let's go home.'

Teresa had replied, 'Let's go home, my love.'

'Turco, what are you doing over there?' yelled the boss. 'The side of the pitch is where you go to piss! Go and get the fucking ball. Go on!'

Turco complied, and then attempted an optimistic drop-goal. The ball wobbled unsteadily through the air and got caught up in a forest of hands. Jorge came away with it and headed for the try line. Two metres short, he felt arms wrap around his legs, others around his chest – Raúl and Santiago had got back just in time to make the tackle – and as he thumped to the earth he knocked the ball on. Scrum restart. It might have only been a training game, but nobody was willing to concede an inch. Passarella watched on, satisfied, chewing on the end of his cigar.

Two hours later, there was a good mood around the changing room. The session had given them a hunger for more games – Mondays always did.

'Sunday we're playing against Córdoba,' the boss was saying. 'They're big lads from up in the hills. They hit hard.'

'So do we,' said Turco. The boss didn't turn his head. He didn't like being interrupted by the boys when he was talking, even though Turco hadn't been a boy for some time.

'Matches like these have to be our bread and butter. You were slow out there today, dragging your feet around like weights . . .'

Gustavo raised his hand like he was at school.

'What is it?'

'It rained, boss. The pitch was a swamp . . .'

'I couldn't give a fuck. If you're afraid of water, you should have stayed home and played draughts with your sister. When you're at training I need you focused, damn it! Any questions?'

Passarella cast his gaze over each of them in turn: they all held their breath. They dressed in silence and left without another word, Raúl the last to go. Passarella put out a hand to stop him.

'What's going on with Mono?'

'I don't know, boss. I waited for him in the usual place. He didn't show up.'

'Find him. Tell him that if he doesn't train tomorrow, he doesn't play on Sunday.'

*

Raúl parked the Guzzi in front of the door to Otilio's building. Because of this idiot, he'd be late to get back home, and Teresa would have finished cooking. She'd put the plate in front of him without a sound. She wouldn't ask how training had gone. She wouldn't say a word. She would just sit there with a stare of cold injury. Fuck Mono for that. And for making him climb three flights of stairs – he couldn't even call him from the street because the shutters were all shut tight, as if there was nobody home.

He knocked twice. Nothing. He sought a glimmer of light underneath the old, peeling door. He could have sent it flying with one kick – but then he would have to explain himself to Otilio's mother, and that crazy woman would probably chase him down the street with a broom. He knocked again. Waited. Nothing.

He turned to go back downstairs when he heard a door open behind him: the neighbour.

'What do you want?' asked a woman, the contours of her face barely visible through the narrow crack between the wall and the door. 'Who are you looking for?'

'Otilio Pascua.'

The woman said nothing, her gaze stayed on him for another moment.

'Are you with the police?'

'No.'

'So why are you looking for him?'

What do you mean? he thought. *I just am – and that's all you need to know. He was supposed to be at training and he never showed up.* But he said nothing. A sense of unease began to creep over him.

He tried again. 'There's nobody home?'

The neighbour's door remained stubbornly motionless; open just wide enough to confirm that the lady was still standing there.

'They were taken away,' she said eventually. She seemed neither upset nor concerned.

'What do you mean, "taken away"?'

No answer was forthcoming. The door had closed.

4

Taken away? Who had given that crazy old woman the idea that they had been taken away? How did she know they hadn't gone to San Justo? Otilio's mother had a brother who lived around there. Maybe his uncle was ill, maybe even dead. What did she mean by 'taken away'?

He needed to talk to Passarella.

The boss lived by himself in Mataderos, a barrio that consisted of little more than scattered blocks of drab residential buildings built to separate the city from the expanse of countryside where the cowherds brought their livestock before delivering them to the slaughterhouses from which it took its name. Raúl had gone home with him once, so that was where he went looking.

'What are you doing here?'

Passarella had opened the door only an inch, much like Mono's neighbour. His beard was unkempt, his eyes bleary and his breathing heavy, as if he had been awoken from a nightmare.

'Are you deaf? I asked you what you're doing here!'

'I need to tell you something, boss.'

'Go on then.'

'Can I come in?'

The older man paused for a moment.

'Wait for me downstairs.' He shut the door.

He reappeared at the entrance to the building ten minutes later. He had put on a white shirt, trimmed his beard, the cigar was clamped between his teeth, his expression sullen: he was the old boss once more.

'So, what is it?'

'Mono . . .'

'What happened?'

'I don't know. He isn't at home.'

'What did his mother say?'

'She wasn't there either. One of their neighbours said they were taken away on Saturday night. Both of them.'

Passarella didn't ask who had taken them away. He didn't ask anything.

'My leg hurts if I stand still for too long,' he said eventually. 'Let's go somewhere else.'

Raúl took a step towards the Guzzi. The boss put a hand on his arm.

'Leave the bike here.' He looked towards a bus that was making its way up from the bottom of the street. 'We'll take that.'

It was ten o'clock at night, the bus was empty. Passarella and Raúl took up seats at the back. For a while, they stared out of the windows in silence as it rumbled along the deserted streets of Mataderos, passing between rows of indistinct, long, narrow buildings, plain brick facades dotted with boarded-up windows and apologetic streetlights providing pale illumination. Night had fallen.

Passarella broke the silence. 'You understand that Mono isn't coming back, right?'

No, Raúl had not understood that.

'He's not coming back,' the boss repeated.

'Why?'

'I don't know, you'd have to ask him.' His tone hardened.

'We'll ask him then.'

'Forget about it. If they come and find you at home without even going to the trouble of waiting until nightfall, they don't mean you to ever come back to that place again!'

'But what could Otilio have done? He was only eighteen.'

'That means nothing to those people.'

'Who are "those people"?'

'Keep your voice down . . .'

'Who are you talking about, boss?'

Passarella put the cigar back in his pocket.

'Listen, I have no intention of getting myself involved in these things.'

'What things? What are you talking about?'

'I'm talking about your country, you imbecile.' He turned his gaze out of the window once more. 'I'm talking about the things that are happening out there. And you'd best keep yourself clear of it. Whatever happened to Mono, whatever stupid thing he did, you just focus on playing rugby.

'Now go on, off you go . . .'

'What about you?'

'I'm going to stay here a bit longer, wait for my leg to stop giving me trouble . . . go on, off you go!'

Raúl climbed out of his seat and walked back up the bus. He rapped on the glass, and the driver stopped. He wanted to think of something else to say before he left, but he knew the boss, he recognised the finality in that tone of voice. He got off without turning back.

5

Mono showed up two days later. His wrists were tied behind his back, bound tightly together by a metal wire that had been wrapped around them twice. His hands were missing. And he had a walnut-sized hole through the back of his head. The rocks that had been placed in his pockets to weigh him down had fallen out and been lost in the depths of the polluted waters of the Río de la Plata, and he had floated to the surface. He returned with his boyish face swollen almost beyond recognition by the water and his eyes half open, an empty gaze into nothingness.

He was found by two locals out fishing. They

grabbed him by an ankle and hauled him out onto the riverbank. They rifled through his pockets: nothing of value. All they found was the rugby club membership card that bore his name and a photo of him with the inquisitive expression that had so often adorned his face – before a 9mm bullet had been put through his head.

It was left to Passarella to identify the body in the morgue that evening. He hobbled in wearing the waterproof jacket that he usually only wore to away games. He had shaved the beard, and even dabbed on a splash of eau de Cologne.

'Are you the father?'

'The coach.'

The duty attendant had learned to keep his questions to himself.

'Follow me.' He seemed bored.

They walked along a seemingly endless warren of corridors with countless doors, the stench of chlorine assailing their nostrils with every step. On the ground behind one of these doors was an open stretcher. On top of it lay Otilio, covered almost entirely by a dirty sheet. One foot poked out from the bottom, still dressed in a white sock.

'There was nowhere else you could have put him?'

'The morgue is full. There was another accident on the motorway.'

'*Another* accident? Who told you this was an accident?'

Passarella bent down and pulled the cloth back from the boy's face.

The attendant began reading from a sheet of paper: 'Otilio Pascua, eighteen years old, born Buenos Aires, 1960. Resident in Coronel Rivadavia 1261 . . . is this him?'

'This is him.' Passarella struggled back to his feet.

The man passed him the sheet of paper. 'Sign here and go home to bed.'

6

The following morning, the whole team showed up at the cemetery. To Raúl's surprise and great relief, he saw Otilio's mother was there. He had feared that she might have suffered a similar fate to her son and he was glad beyond words to see her alive and safe. But the agony of her grief was palpable – her face swollen with tears, her lips tightly sealed in a grimace of staunch silence. She was standing off to one side of the grave, watched over by a few relatives who seemed to be trying to keep her away from everyone else present.

From the rugby club, only Passarella was missing. The players waited for him, surprised that he had not been the first to arrive. For as long as they had known him, the boss had never missed a single training session. Never. And now that one of his boys was being buried . . . he wasn't there.

It was Turco who eventually approached Raúl, who everyone knew had been as close as family to the deceased.

'How come the boss isn't here?'

'I don't know. When I went to see him, he seemed a bit . . . strange.'

'You saw him? Where?'

'I went over to his place the other night. I wanted to tell him that Mono had gone missing.'

'And what did he say?'

'He didn't want to say anything. But it felt like he already knew everything.'

'There is nothing to know. They murdered him and washed their hands of it.'

'They shot him in the back of the head, Turk.'

'And if they had shot him in the face? What difference would it have made? And if it had been you they'd shot instead of Mono, what difference would it have made? They've fucked up the country.'

'The boss says that . . .'

Turk raised his voice. 'If the boss had something to say, he should be here to say it!'

The priest glanced over at them, then lifted the thurible with the incense. He spoke in Latin, haltingly, swallowing his words. He appeared distracted, as if he was there by chance alone. When he intoned Otilio's name, the boys' heads dropped, each taking a moment of blessed quiet to remember their fallen friend. It was all over within five minutes. Four undertakers stepped forward, took a corner each, and slid the coffin into the grave. There was not even time for people to cast a fistful of soil into the hole: the undertakers grabbed their spades and got straight to work. They were in a rush too.

As soon as it was over, Raúl went over to Otilio's mother. He had no idea what he was going to say, but it seemed the right thing to do: to let her know he was there, that he would always be there if she needed him. She seemed to have shrunk in stature, and she was frailer than he remembered her, as if the pain had eaten away at her body. Raúl cast around for something to say, but it was Otilio's mother who spoke first.

'I went to every police station in the city . . .'

Her voice was low and resolute, that of a woman who knew exactly what she wanted to say. Raúl waited for her to continue.

'I thought maybe they were holding him somewhere, maybe they would give him back to me.'

Them again. Who were they? Raúl didn't ask, it felt like an inappropriate question. He stood there while she blew her nose and put her handkerchief back in her bag.

'What did they tell you?'

'The same thing every time. That they knew nothing about it. That the people who took my son were not from the police.'

'And did you believe them?'

She seemed to straighten up suddenly, as if he had touched a forgotten nerve. She stared straight at Raúl.

'What do you care if I believed them?'

'I'm sorry . . .'

'What would you have done?'

Raúl glanced over at the rest of the team who were standing by the gates to the cemetery. Passarella had not arrived, so it was up to him to dismiss them to go home.

'I don't know,' he replied. The woman looked at him for a moment, as if struggling with herself, then she pulled a crumpled notebook out of her bag and flicked through the pages rapidly. Sheets of graph paper filled with small, neat letters. That was Mono's handwriting: patient, focused. It was the same way he had played rugby. She placed the notebook in his hand.

'I found this at the bottom of his bag, in with all the muddy jerseys.'

'Why are you giving it to me?'

'Because Otilio trusted you. He would always tell me that when you took him on your motorbike, he felt as protected as a pope.' She tried to force a smile. 'I haven't read it. I don't want to know what it says. But if they killed him because of the things he wrote there, it means he was doing something right. Read it for both of us.'

Raúl nodded, almost out of politeness, then put the notebook in his pocket without a further glance.

7

'What's that?'

Teresa nodded towards the red notebook sitting on the table between the dirty dinner plates and two empty bottles of beer. Raúl had told her about the cemetery, the tear-swollen face of Otilio's mother, the priest's half-hearted words. He wondered whether anyone had told him how old Mono had been when he was killed, whether someone had explained how they had murdered his friend. It felt as though the priest, aloof and stiff as a rake, had offended Raúl more than Mono's killers.

Teresa had listened without interrupting. They ate with their heads bowed and their eyes on their plates, each trapped in their own thoughts. Raúl mopped up the sauce at the bottom of the plate with a piece of bread, then used his knife to gather the breadcrumbs that had fallen onto the table, rearranging them in a line like soldiers on parade. He wasn't ready for dinner to end, for the moment when he would have to look up and they would have to admit that some intrusive force had entered their lives. There was an image in his head that was bothering him even more than Mono's death: Passarella had told the team about the metal wire that had been wrapped twice around their friend's wrists. No need for a thick rope or a pair of handcuffs: a pliable metal wire had been enough. And then they had cut off his hands . . .

He glanced at Teresa and saw that she was staring into the distance, her thoughts far away.

'What are you thinking?' he asked.

'Nothing much,' she said, snapping back.

'Tell me.'

'I'm just sad. And I was thinking . . . I dunno . . . just that it's awful that you didn't get the chance to say goodbye to each other. When it's my turn to go, I want to be able to say goodbye to all my friends.'

Raúl shivered. When it came to his turn to go, he didn't want to know in advance.

He pulled out the notebook and placed it on the table, pushing it between the dirty plates.

'What's that?'

'It was Mono's. His mum gave it to me.'

He opened it, began to flick through the pages. The neat handwriting was a thing of beauty. Raúl's was another story entirely – he wrote with the same ferocity as his father mended shoes, letters scratched heavily into the page to hold the words fast, like nails holding soles in place. Otilio had never known his father; he had learned to write by imitating the patient handwriting of his schoolteacher, one letter at a time, rounding off every vowel with a flick of the pen.

'What does it say?' asked Teresa.

Raúl began to lift fragments from every page.

'Here it mentions a game against Boca, it's dated September 21st – Mono scored two tries that they won't forget . . . This is something from one of his classes. October 10th, he wrote that they wanted to kick him out of chemistry class, but he couldn't care less if they did, he was done with school anyway. "The time for hiding in a classroom is over, the time for waiting is over . . ."'

'Waiting for what?'

'It's not clear. He doesn't say.' He turned over a couple more pages. Then he stopped.

'This is from November 18th.'

Raúl skimmed the page silently.

'What does it say?'

'Did you know Otilio was a member of the Union of Secondary School Students?'

'Who? Mono?'

Teresa took the notebook out of his hands and began to turn the pages slowly. Suddenly she stopped and placed a finger on the page.

'Do you remember when they ended the student discount for textbooks and they had that protest?'

'The one in front of the ministry? Yeah, I remember that.'

'Otilio was there.'

'He never mentioned it to me . . .'

'And he never mentioned that he'd enlisted with those lunatics from the Union. Listen to this: "The government has decided to stop us from carrying out any form of protest. They have banned any atheist or anti-nationalist demonstrations. But what does atheism have to do with our civil liberties? They want to stop us, but not this time . . ."'

'What else?' asked Raúl.

'There's nothing else. The notebook ends there.'

'That's why they took him away? There were police everywhere that day, I remember it . . .'

'They'll know everyone in the Union,' said Teresa slowly.

They. Again. *They* who had taken Otilio, who had

tied his wrists behind his back with metal wire, who had sawn off his hands, who had murdered him like a stray dog, without even looking him in the eyes. *They* who'd left him to be consumed by the waters of the Río de la Plata. *They* had known, he had not.

'I had no idea . . .' he faltered. He seemed to be trying to justify himself. His voice cracked and shattered like glass, the full impact sending shards spinning uncontrollably in every direction. The remaining words caught in his throat and were extinguished by a desperate sob. Teresa moved the plates to one side and stretched across the table to hold his head, to keep him steady and protected between her hands as he wept, the sobs rising from his chest and his thoughts carving a permanent scar in him, ending one phase of his life and leaving him with the dawning realisation that nothing would go back to the way it had been before. Not for him. Not for Teresa. Nothing and nobody would go back to the way it was before.

Teresa lowered her face to his, her lips brushing against his hair.

'You won't do anything stupid, will you, Raúl? You won't get yourself killed? Promise me, Raúl. You have to promise me that you won't get yourself killed . . .'

Raúl kept his eyes firmly shut. Said nothing. Thought nothing.

8

It was Sunday. Matchday. The team from Córdoba arrived after an eight-hour bus journey, their eyes hazy and swollen from sleep. They had been informed that one of the Club La Plata players – one they remembered as being quick and agile – had been found dead in the river, and they had no idea how to deal with the subject, whether to mention it or whether to act like nothing had happened.

'That story has nothing to do with us,' their coach had told them. He had made them stand on parade before they left, lined up silently in front of the bus with the engine already rumbling.

'We're going to La Plata, playing our regular game and coming home.' The players had nodded dubiously and climbed aboard.

They had travelled overnight, crossing the country until they found themselves on the La Plata pitch, warming their studs on ground that seemed like one long furrow, bone-dry from the salt and the sea breeze. That was what happened with rugby pitches facing the ocean, you ended up having to be more cautious about your next step than you were about your opponents. Assuming there was an opposition team to be wary of: three minutes before the whistle was due to blow, only the team from Córdoba were on the pitch.

La Plata were still in the changing room. Sitting, kitted out, ready. Silent. Passarella glanced at his watch. He levered himself up, the backrest of the bench taking the brunt of his weight. He was unsteady for a moment on his one good leg.

'One minute, everyone on the pitch.'

Nobody moved.

'Anyone who isn't feeling up to it is welcome to go home.' No anger in his voice.

Santiago, the Native American, spoke up. 'We're going to ask the referee for a minute's silence.'

The boss swung his head around towards him.

'No!'

'Why not?'

'We're here to go out on the pitch and play and nothing else. The other stuff stays off the pitch.'

'"The other stuff" was called Otilio,' said Jorge.

'Have you read the newspapers?' Passarella asked him.

'No, I haven't . . . what do the papers have to do with anything?'

'There wasn't a single fucking line about Otilio. Like it never happened. The world outside has already moved on.'

'If we don't hold a minute's silence, I'm not playing,' said Turco.

'Me neither,' added Mariano.

Passarella looked at Raúl. 'And you?'

Everyone's eyes turned towards him. It dawned on Raúl that his teammates were unable to call which side he would come down on, which made him furious.

'It looks like nobody will be playing today, boss,' he replied firmly.

Passarella held his position, resting against the door like a crooked branch. They could hear his jaws working as he chewed the end of his cigar furiously.

'You don't understand . . .' he muttered at last. Then he turned and walked out of the changing room.

*

La Plata walked onto the pitch without a sound, faces drawn, black socks tied around their arms as makeshift armbands. There was no applause from the crowd, no response at all. They were waiting to see what would happen.

Passarella limped out to the halfway line.

'Listen,' he said to the referee, 'we're going to hold a minute's silence before we start.' He looked uncomfortable. 'One of my boys died recently, a good kid . . .'

'You need union authorisation for that,' said the referee. Passarella turned to look at his players: they were waiting. He lowered his voice to a growl, every word cutting like broken glass.

'Fuck the union, asshole . . .'

'How dare you . . .'

'How dare I speak to you like that? Is that what you're asking me? How dare I call you an asshole?' Passarella lurched closer and pressed a finger into the man's chest. 'If you don't let my boys hold the minute's silence, there will be no game today. And then what will you tell your union?'

The referee cleared his throat and took a moment to restore some dignity.

'Fine, one minute. But then we start.'

*

At first there was nothing but the eyes of Otilio's teammates looking for somewhere to fix their gaze. A minute can drag on for a lifetime, as drawn out as a slow death. It moves forward slowly, marking time, singing a song of identical stanzas. A minute is the sound of seconds that never meet, that never end. And yet they did end, and when they did the referee blew his whistle, and then the unimaginable happened – a spell that fell over the pitch. Down on the grass, nobody moved. Up in the stands, nobody sat back down. Everyone remained fixed, frozen, arms by their sides, the ball forgotten. Everyone waited for a bit more time to pass because a minute was short, too short for Mono, too short for that miserable death with the metal wire wrapped around his wrists and the muzzle of the pistol pressed into the back of his head. And anyway, where had they finished Mono off? What had he carried away in his eyes from the moment of the murder? Night? Sky? Water? The face of one of those scumbags?

No, one minute was not enough, another one was needed, and then another still. And in the meantime, nobody moved – bound together, committed to stretching out the time, expanding it to fill the life that Mono had lived, which had been torn away from him when he was just eighteen years old. Assholes . . . eighteen years old and you think one minute will suffice? Four minutes passed, then five. Six. It was of no consequence, nobody was in any rush to play, nobody in a rush to forget. Eight minutes. Nine.

Ten.

For ten long minutes that silence held. Then the colour came rushing back to the scene, the players walked over to take up their positions on the pitch, smiles breaking out, beautiful and powered by emotions that could not be articulated. The referee blew his whistle, although his mind was elsewhere, as were the minds of the opposition, upstanding boys who had come down from Córdoba for a game of rugby and had instead come face to face with life and death, all in the space of one day, all in one minute that lasted ten.

To spite the bastards who had put an end to Mono's life.

*

There was no drama in the match itself. Passarella's boys won without ever feeling they had been tested. When the final whistle went, the applause that rained down on them from the stands spoke of something more, something tangible.

There was only one man who left the ground without applauding. Small, around forty years old, he too walking with a pronounced limp, yet moving at a pace driven by urgency and nerves. He leant on an iron-tipped cane, one leg stiff as a post, one hand in the pocket of his waterproof coat, a thoughtful expression on his face. He skirted his way around the contemptuous rabble with their excitable exchanges, paying no heed to ill-judged grins that spoke to the pretence of a long afternoon's celebration winding down.

He limped his way to the street and looked around in search of something. To the casual observer, his creased clothes, pallid face and unkempt beard spoke of a mid-ranking office worker, the type of person you might expect to encounter buying a paper cone of roast chestnuts from one of the street vendors along Calle Florida in the middle of the day, in the full knowledge that his presence would not be missed in the office.

In truth, Ricardo Montonero was a soldier. More than that, he was an officer, equivalent to a captain, even though he had never fought in a war and had no assistant waiting for him outside the ground and no vehicle waiting to pick him up, only the public bus that stopped in front of him, already packed with bodies. Montonero tried to clear some space with his cane before two people eventually hauled him aboard. Poor old guy, remarked one; a poor cripple, replied the other. But Montonero kept quiet. Nobody needed to know who he was and why he had travelled all the way out to the stadium at La Plata.

9

Three quarters of an hour later, Montonero hobbled off the bus onto the Avenida del Libertador. He walked towards a white-brick mansion with the coat of arms of the republic emblazoned above the entrance, and bedecked by a row of high, narrow windows sealed by iron bars. A perfectly manicured lawn and a colonnade in front of the façade boldly announced that this was a place for the powerful and wealthy.

Once upon a time, this building had served as the School of Naval Mechanics, and it retained the acronym, ESMA (*Escuela Superior de Mecánica de la*

Armada in Spanish). The cadets had been sent to learn their craft elsewhere and the white mansion on the Libertador had been commandeered by Batallón 601 of the Military Intelligence Service. These were the street sweepers of the military junta – those charged with 'cleaning up the country'.

Montonero entered the building and crossed a bare entrance hall with marble flooring and polished stone walls. Two men in plain clothes were leaning against one of the walls and chatting, but they straightened and threw listless salutes as he passed. Montonero climbed the stairs to the first floor and faced the long, narrow corridor with a single window at the far end and rows of closed doors on both left and right. There were no remnants in here of the military aura projected by the external façade of the building. He used his good leg to brush a few cigarette butts out of his way and entered his office, which was little more than a cubbyhole: a desk, two chairs, a telephone, a stationery tray with four pencils in it and a metal locker pushed up against the wall.

Montonero opened the locker. Inside, a mirror hung on the door and a coat-hanger held his lieutenant commander's uniform. He stripped off his raincoat, suit, shirt and socks and placed them with meticulous care in the locker. He glanced into the mirror – flabby, lopsided, the left leg firmly planted on the ground like the needle point of a compass, the right a crooked S-shape, as if it had been detached and replaced in a hurry.

He examined the misshapen, pale flesh of his body, the few remaining strands of hair on his head, the protruding bones in his shoulders, and the sagging backside. He ran a hand over his beer-swollen gut with a grimace – disgusting. He was under no illusions about his physical attraction, and it even gave him a moment of satisfaction. Anyone else cursed with the same risible physique and the same busted leg would have been reduced to gathering cardboard boxes for a bed along the Avenida Central. But not him. He was Lieutenant Commander Ricardo Genulfo Montonero, a former clerk at the Ministry of Education whose elevated sense of patriotism had seen him promoted into the ranks of the Navy over the heads of colleagues who had remained trapped in their worthless lives in worthless homes with miserable wives and half-witted children, who chose to spend what little money they earned shuffling papers around and going to watch rugby matches when he would gladly have that rabble from La Plata locked up – give them something to think about beyond their championship. He would see to it that Colonel Benavides found out exactly what they were up to . . .

The thought of Benavides wiped the smirk off his face. He quickly finished getting dressed, his fingers stumbling over the golden buttons of the double-breasted jacket, the knot of his tie coming out too tight. He stared into the mirror once more: the uniform was drooping off him, loose and awkward, as if he had borrowed it from a much larger man. He sighed at his ridiculous visage . . . this damned job with the Army wasn't for him; but it served its purpose, kept him safe and even offered the occasional fleeting satisfaction. He rested a hand on the holster attached to his belt and felt the weight of the Luger, then studied the insignias, the aiguillette and the other decorations he had to pin to himself every time he reported to the colonel. Still, it could be worse, he reasoned. He clicked his heels, slammed the locker shut and left.

*

'Attention!' Montonero stiffened and gave a lopsided salute.

'At ease . . .' continued Colonel Benavides without looking. He was the younger man by a few years and everything nature had stripped away from Montonero, it had bestowed upon Benavides with treacherous generosity. Tall, slim, broad-shouldered, straight-backed and with a withering gaze, the colonel wore a light linen outfit with his initials embroidered on the shirt. He never wore the uniform: it was a matter of status, he explained. He had taken over half of the second floor for his office and had set it out like a parade ground. It was said that he took his orders directly from President Videla himself, and that he started every day by reporting to the president on the national security situation: those arrested, those interrogated, those assassinated. What Videla said to him in return, or the orders he received – only Benavides knew. Montonero received only fragments of news, emotions and suspicions.

'Well, Montonero, did you enjoy the party? Plenty of eye candy in the stands?'

Benavides's gaze was still fixed out of the window, which in this office had the grand dimensions of an archway and a view facing directly onto the traffic on the avenida.

'They play well,' replied Montonero. 'A solid scrum and a couple of quick wingers. Unless they lose to Resistencia, they'll take home the title this season.'

The colonel looked up. 'And why should we give a shit?' he asked bluntly.

No reason: it was just that Montonero liked rugby. Once upon a time, he had been a referee, a lifetime ago when his leg was still in one piece.

'So we can shelve this operation? We're sure there are no other loose cannons among them who might become a pain in the arse further down the line?'

These were the moments in his job that Montonero lived for. Shelve the operation . . . or stay on them like attack dogs? What did this little bitch of a colonel know about the right course of action to take in the interests of national security in this situation? Montonero would be the one to decide whether the operation would be shut down, when there was no further need to call on the boys from the floor below to poke around in the lives of those he was interested in. And Montonero had no desire to shut down this particular operation. Not yet.

'There is still something I'm not sure about.'

'Go on.'

'The boy, the one we arrested . . .'

'Pascua. He was a delinquent. What about him?'

'His teammates decided to hold a minute's silence for him today, before the game.'

'So what, Montonero. Now we're going to concern ourselves with those who stay quiet too?'

'Of course not, colonel.'

'Better quiet than communists.'

'Better quiet than criminals.'

'So where's the problem?'

'They were silent for ten minutes.'

'What do you mean, ten minutes?'

'Ten minutes, colonel. I counted.'

'And the crowd?'

'The same.'

'Ten minutes . . .'

'Not so much as the buzz of a mosquito, colonel.'

'I blame those morons who were supposed to get rid of the boy! They put two stones in his pockets, threw him into the river and wandered off!'

'If I may, colonel . . .'

'A corpse always leads to a funeral. And a funeral always leads to trouble.'

'Colonel . . .'

'What is it? What do you want?!'

Montonero's leg was aching, he could feel it throbbing at the spot where they had inserted the three nails in an attempt to hold the bones together.

'May I take a seat?'

He sat down without waiting for permission.

'Those ten minutes' silence on the pitch today weren't a funeral. They were a provocation. A prearranged protest against us.'

The word provocation always set Benavides on edge. His heart beat a little faster.

There was silence in the room for a moment while

the colonel thought. Montonero could sense the anger rising on the other side of the desk. 'You stick close to those little kids, Montonero,' said Benavides, his voice little more than a whisper. 'I want to know what they're thinking, what they're planning, who they're meeting, who they're sleeping with. I want to know everything. Take a few men if you need . . .'

Montonero rose to his feet.

'You will hear no more from those people, *mi coronel*.'

'One more thing . . . that cane . . .'

'What's wrong with my cane?'

'Where did you get it from? I mean, the silver handle and all the rest of it . . .'

'From an antiques dealer,' replied Montonero cautiously. He thought for a moment. 'We shut down his shop. He was a member of the CGTA trade union.'

'It makes you look like a faggot. A cane with a silver knob on the end is a faggot's accessory. Get rid of it.'

Montonero shifted back almost imperceptibly.

'Is that an order?'

'What do you think?'

'I think it's an order . . .' He gave a weak salute. He crossed Benavides's office, as vast to him as the deck of an aircraft carrier, his cane held underneath his arm like a public official in the colonies. With every step he wondered if the damaged leg would finally betray him and send him to the floor in a pile of shattered bones. He – and it – held firm, all the way to the door.

As soon as he was outside, Montonero rested his shoulders on the wall of the corridor, closed his eyes and sucked air in and out like a bellows. For this too, he swore, those lowlifes from La Plata would be made to pay.

10

'What's the matter? You got lead stuck up your arses today?'

The team looked sheepishly at the boss. They knew he was right. There was no way they were training the way they should – the passes were half-hearted, their tackling was pathetic, their heads were elsewhere. They were like strangers thrown together by chance.

'Mariano? What are you doing all the way back there – tugging yourself off?' Passarella had caught up with them in the middle of the pitch. 'And you, Santiago, you call that hitting a ruck? Are you serious?

This isn't the standard, boys! This isn't anything like it!'

He spat his cigar onto the ground, put the ball under his arm, and marched off towards the changing rooms. Training was over.

*

Back in the showers, the boys let the water wash over them in silence. It was as if they had never met before.

Turco was the one who eventually broke the spell. 'Those pigs from the military killed him,' he muttered, his voice echoing off the tiles.

'Quiet!' someone snapped.

'We're always being quiet,' retorted Raúl.

'And you're right to be,' growled Passarella. No one had heard him come in. He was standing like a crooked olive tree at the entrance to the shower room. Everyone fell silent and averted their eyes. An unmistakable veil of mistrust had fallen between the team and their coach.

'You won't bring Mono back to life by crying all over the place. Think about your next game. And keep yourselves out of trouble.'

The moment Passarella left, Santiago spat out a mouthful of soap and swept it away under his heel. Nothing else happened, no one else spoke.

*

Raúl was among the first to get dressed. He knew what he had to do. He left the changing room and went in search of Passarella, who he found sitting on the pavement, scribbling notes on his papers. Plans for the next match.

'I'll give you a ride home, boss.' It was not a question.

'I'm not getting on that wreck and you know it,' said Passarella, nodding towards Raúl's Guzzi. 'I'll take the bus.' He folded the papers in his pocket, got to his feet, and hobbled towards the stop. Raúl walked alongside him, pushing the bike.

'Why weren't you at Mono's funeral?'

Passarella kept walking.

'They're all talking about it in there,' Raúl thumbed towards the changing rooms. 'Wondering.'

'Wondering what?'

'If you were scared.'

The boss passed the bus stop and kept walking, his eyes fixed on the uneven paving stones.

'Idiots . . .' he grumbled at last. 'I've never been scared of anything.'

A pathetic response, thought Raúl. He climbed onto the Guzzi and kick-started the engine.

'I know guys like the ones that murdered Pascua,' the boss said abruptly. Raúl waited, the engine burbling softly. 'They murder poor sods like him and convince themselves it's some great patriotic service to the Fatherland. There's no use arguing with them.

If you run into them, best to just cross the street and leave them well alone.'

'How do you know guys like that?'

Passarella said nothing. He shook his head: he knew and that was all there was to it. Raúl pulled Otilio's notebook from his pocket and rested it on the petrol tank, one hand on top of it, keeping it shut.

'This belonged to Mono. It says he was active in the *Movimiento Estudiantil*. The ones behind the protest in October.'

Passarella wanted to stretch out a hand towards the notebook, Raúl could see it in the suffering in his eyes, in the veil of anger that fell over his gaze for the briefest moment. It was a momentary lapse, a sign of weakness, and it passed without leaving a trace in his voice.

'Get rid of it and forget what it says.'

'Why?'

'Why would they come for me next? Surely it stops with Mono.'

'It didn't stop with Hernan.'

'What do you mean?' Hearing Hernan's name was like a punch to the gut. Their scrum-half had had his car hijacked on the Pan-American Highway a few months earlier. He had been shot and killed.

'That was them.'

'How do you know?'

Passarella sighed. 'I don't. Not for sure. But it's more plausible than hijackers. He was found blindfolded and riddled with bullets. And yet there were no shells to be found anywhere. Would hijackers do that? Kill him somewhere else and then dump his body? I don't think so.'

Raúl stared at him, unable to process the information. Then, his gaze still distant, he revved up the Guzzi and took off down the road.

11

'Is it true what they're saying?'

Turco pulled his hands out of the tub where he had been currying the cowhide for the past fifteen minutes. Gonzalo looked at him expectantly. Gonzalo was the oldest worker at the tannery; he had grown up in that place and was never found wanting when someone needed to be shown the ropes. An old-fashioned sort.

'What are they saying?' Turco asked.

'They're saying that the *yutas* took someone from your squad.'

Turco looked down at his hands, where the skin was cracked from the bating and the acids used in the tanning process. He wiped them down on his leather apron. One of these days, the flesh underneath would be exposed like a steak.

'What else?'

'That they murdered him because he was a communist,' said Gonzalo.

His blunt approach to questions was one of the traits that endeared Gonzalo to Turco. Only now, he had no answer.

'I don't know if he was a communist.'

'Well, if he wasn't, why did they kill him?'

Turco's face darkened. 'He was only a kid . . .'

'And what about you?'

'What about me?'

'What are you doing, Turco? You're not a kid anymore.'

'I do my own thing. What else can I do? I know how to tan a cowhide. I know how to bring down an opponent on the pitch if he's heading for the try line.'

'And how do you bring him down?'

Turco smiled and ran a finger over his teeth.

'I'll break his leg if I have to. As long as I'm on the pitch, he's not getting past me.'

A siren went off to announce the end of the shift. Gonzalo removed his apron in silence.

'They've already passed you, Turco,' he said quietly, after a moment. He looked around. 'Wait for me outside, near the bike rack.'

Turco nodded.

*

'We're meeting up with the others here on Saturday evening . . .' Gonzalo said.

It was raining outside. He and Turco were resting against their bikes, the street was deserted. Turco was famished and his legs were aching after nine hours on his feet spent scrubbing the hides with the hard bristles of his brush.

'A few people who work in the factories along the

Carretera Norte will be coming,' Gonzalo went on. 'Workers. People like you and me. We're looking to set up a kind of trade union.'

'The trade unions have been dissolved.'

Gonzalo smiled. 'We haven't set it up yet. How can they dissolve it? So, how about it? Are you coming?'

'I don't know . . .' Turco hesitated. And it was the truth.

'Are you scared?'

'I have a game. I usually go to bed early the night before.'

'Don't go soft on me, Turco. We'll have a quick chat with the others and you'll be home in time for beddy-bye. Agreed?'

Turco lifted his bicycle off the rack, climbed on and pushed down on the pedal.

'Maybe . . .' he grunted, without turning his head. Gonzalo smiled.

*

From his vantage point across the street, Montonero smiled too. But this was a different smile, as if disappointed. Gonzalo turned towards him and the two exchanged a glance and the slightest nod of acknowledgement. Then each went his separate way.

12

At training the next day, Turco was leaden. He put in a half-hearted tackle on Mariano to stop him on the way to the try line, but the younger man showed him a clean pair of heels, sweeping past with the ball held close to his chest without even changing direction. Turco scrambled to recover and as Mariano was held up in a cover tackle by Santiago, the prop roared in with a swinging arm that almost took Mariano's head off.

'What the fuck was that about?' bellowed Mariano, rising to his feet. He lifted his fist to swing a punch at

Turco, but was held back by his teammates. Turco just stood and stared, lost in his own world.

'You fucking asshole,' spat Mariano.

Turco bent down to tie a shoelace, as if he'd not heard, avoiding eye-contact with the others.

Passarella arrived: 'Okay, okay, ball down,' he said wearily. 'Hey, cut it out, Mariano. We all right here? Good. We'll restart with a scrum. Let's go, no harm done.'

*

After the session, Passarella went looking for Turco in the changing rooms. He found him in the showers and when Turco was washed and in his towel, the boss took him over to a quiet corner to speak.

'Sit down.'

Turco flopped onto the bench. His towel was too short and his bare arms stood out like the branches of an oak tree.

'What's gotten into you, Turco? If you play like that on Sunday, Corrientes will put thirty points on us.'

'It's nothing. It's just that . . .'

Passarella crouched next to his player, their heads closer. He looked like a priest hearing confession.

'What is it, Turco?'

'Mono. We held a funeral for him.'

'I know.'

'And then what?'

'We dedicated ten magnificent minutes of silence to him last Sunday.'

'And then what?' Stubborn as a child, the Turk. He was waiting for the boss to explode. But Passarella kept his cool, stood back up, massaged his crocked leg.

'And then we hope not to have any more funerals,' said the boss with a sigh. 'Go home, Turco. Get some rest and think about the title we have to win. That's it. Everything else can wait.'

*

But Turco did not go home. He felt like a common criminal, ashamed of that cheap shot on Mariano. What had gotten into him? In truth, he knew the answer: first Mono, then Gonzalo with that offer of the meeting. Life was starting to move too quickly for his liking.

He waited for Mariano to step out of the showers.

'I'm sorry about earlier, bro . . .'

'Forget about it, Turco.' Mariano had the physique of a wardrobe, but he was a soft touch at heart. Every so often he would show up at training with a box full of warm bread, fresh from the oven. Everyone loved Mariano. Except his opponents.

'Are you going for a beer?' asked Mariano. But Turco's mind was elsewhere.

'Listen, you were in the trade union, right?'

'Before.'

'Before what?'

Mariano waved his hand in a backward motion through the air. 'A lifetime ago. Before they dissolved it. Why do you ask?'

'Someone from work – down at the tannery. Asked me to go with him to a meeting. They want to revive the trade union.'

'They're out of their minds.'

'Possibly.'

'Are you also out of your mind, Turco?'

'No, I'm not out of my mind. But if I don't do something, I might really lose it.'

'So what do you want from me?'

'The meeting is tonight. I'm not going alone – I don't know anything about this stuff . . .'

Mariano cocked his head and stared at him with something close to pity.

'The whole thing with Mono really got to you, huh?'

'Everything is starting to get to me, Mariano. So what do you say, are you coming?'

*

The meeting took place in front of the entrance to the tannery. Turco and Mariano arrived on foot, and were there on the dot.

'Who's he?' asked Gonzalo when he saw that Turco wasn't alone.

'My name's Mariano, I'm a teammate of his . . .' came the reply.

'He's on our side,' said Turco. 'He knows a bit about these things.'

'Who else did you tell that we would be here?'

'Nobody,' replied Turco.

Gonzalo looked at him carefully: he wasn't lying.

'I'm happy to see you here,' he said eventually.

'But we have to go early,' Turco replied quickly.

'I know, you said, there's a game tomorrow.'

'Corrientes are tough bastards.'

Gonzalo nodded. 'With those guys, you'll have to control possession and hold it until you die,' he said. 'Their backline hasn't lost a ball all season.'

Turk looked at him curiously.

'What would you know about it? You haven't watched a game in your life.'

'I read about it in *Clarín*, that's how . . .' Gonzalo grinned and then looked over towards the tannery gates. 'Shall we go?'

'As long as we hurry up,' said Turco, unable to hide the edginess in his voice.

13

At the game on Sunday, the crowd had doubled in size. Partly the result of the club's winning record, which would be enough to see them take home the title, and partly after word had gone around regarding the ten minutes' silence for the young boy who had been murdered. Nobody had written about it, nobody had spoken about it, yet that challenge to the military and their enforcers, which consisted of silence and nothing more, had travelled the length and breadth of Argentina – in every corner of every barrio, in every cafetìn, at every bus stop, word went around that something was stirring in La Plata.

Out on the pitch something was stirring too. Passarella's boys were back to their old selves again, the set-plays working like clockwork, the forwards fanning out around the pitch, showing up everywhere, the ball hitting its target every time. Twelve tries the difference by full time. Just like the good old days.

When it came down to it, they were still young boys at heart. Jorge, Gabriel, Santiago, Raúlito. Mono would forever remain stitched into their hearts, but life had to go on, and at that age life is a maelstrom, no less so in Argentina, and no less so in the dark days of the junta, because twenty years old is a forceful whirlwind that meets you head-on and blurs your vision and scrambles your thoughts and leaves you with no time for regrets and no time to mourn the dead. They had held that ten minutes' silence on a whim and it had been a beautiful moment – audacious, brave, a blow against the faceless ghouls that haunted people's nightmares. But they had to move on. They had to play. And to win. That was for Mono too.

None of them noticed Ricardo Montonero, who had hobbled back into his position in the stands, swallowed up by his waterproof jacket. And even if they had spotted the lopsided figure, who among them knew Montonero? He was just another fan, one who this time even raised his hands with the others to applaud the scorching try-scoring pace of *el pibe* Gabriel and the unrelenting tackles by the wardrobe that was Jorge. Montonero left at the end of the game, limping but content, holding on to the rail with both hands as he climbed down the stairs of the stand, wishing he still had his cane. He was still full of resentment at having to give it up, but nevertheless he had enjoyed the game. Those boys were tough. And he had also enjoyed putting together the little programme he had prepared for that evening . . . if only his leg would stop hurting quite so much, if only the colonel had not been such a pain in the arse about his cane . . .

*

That night, Raúl and Teresa made love, taking their time, gazing into one another's eyes until it was over.

'We have to choose to live,' Teresa said when they were done, her hand resting on Raúl's forehead as if she could convey all her thoughts to him telepathically. She was troubled. Distressed about things that were yet to come but that she could feel in her bones, like an arthritis sufferer could sense storms on the horizon.

'Every day, every moment . . .' she carried on, 'live it as if it's the last.'

Raúl was no good at these conversations. They made him feel awkward and distant. It was as if someone had pushed a script into his hand – hey, read this! – and he was forced to improvise, make the right impression, adopt a suitable vocal register. What did it mean to live every day and every moment? What need was there to live it as if it were the last? He was not seeking last moments; it was not yet the time. Albeit now, after Mono's murder, the realisation that every story had its end had hit him like a boulder.

He tried to compartmentalise the memories, to organise them as separate snatches in time: the last time he had seen Mono; the last time Mono had ridden on his motorbike; the last time he had given him a lift to the pitch. Then he began to think about how his own life had already seen so many final moments: the last time he had seen his father before the cirrhosis claimed his liver, and with it his life; the last time he had cried, after which he had felt ashamed. It had not been for Mono, but a year earlier, when the boss had left him out of the squad for messing about too much in training and he had been relegated to watching the game from a hidden vantage point behind the door of the changing room like a thief, disgraced and ridden with guilt.

'And what if this life isn't good enough for us?' Raúl asked suddenly.

'What do you mean?'

'It wasn't good enough for Mono.'

Teresa slid her hands down to cup his face.

'Otilio is gone, Raúl. Promise me you won't get yourself into trouble too, that you'll be happy just playing rugby.'

I promise, I promise, thought Raúl. But he was speaking from slumber. He fell asleep and it was immediately forgotten.

*

Hugo Passarella was not asleep. There was no particular reason, just too many thoughts occupying his head. He had let the bus carry him as far as the central business district, the *Microcentro*, and now he was walking along with his hands in his pockets, dragging his offending leg along Calle Florida.

He stopped in front of the lights of a cinema and examined the posters. They were advertising an old war film featuring John Wayne in a navy uniform. He decided to enter. He found a place in the back row and sat down without even removing his overcoat.

John Wayne had the manner of a man who had only ever seen war in a script, fresh and smart in his neatly pressed colonel's uniform. Wars on the big screen never seemed to capture the true sense of dread of a real conflict, Passarella mused. He tilted his head back. He drifted off.

*

'Your team's games are more enjoyable,' a voice was saying next to him.

Passarella jolted awake. A short man in a white raincoat had taken the seat next to him, gaunt and pallid features expressionless.

'How's the leg, Passarella?'

'Montonero? What are you doing here?'

'I'm watching the film.'

'Don't bullshit me.'

'Cripples like us need to look out for each other, Passarella . . .'

'What do you want?'

'I watched all of your matches. You're too slow to the breakdown, but you have a second row that's worth the title all on its own. Those boys are hard as nails. My compliments.'

'Leave me in peace, Montonero. It's been a rough week.'

Montonero left the other man to return to the film and for a few minutes he followed along in silence. Then he started talking again, his eyes never straying from the screen. His voice was measured and emotionless.

'You're to withdraw from the championship, Passarella. Immediately. Otherwise your boys won't live to see the final game.'

Passarella twisted his body around and grabbed the collar of Montonero's raincoat.

'What are you looking for, Montonero? You've already had one leg broken for match-fixing when you refereed! Do you want me to break the other one?'

Passarella felt the tip of a cane pressing into his stomach. Then he realised it was not a cane, but the muzzle of Montonero's pistol.

'Take your hands off me, asshole.'

Passarella let him go.

'What do you want from me?'

'I'll ask the questions.'

Passarella shifted his weight to put a few centimetres between them and to get a better look at the other man. The angled nose buried in the middle of a face better suited to a smug and self-satisfied student, the peevish and ill-mannered tone, the greasy collar of the raincoat. It was Montonero, no doubt about it. But he felt like he was seeing him for the first time.

'What are you looking at?'

'Who gave you that gun, Montonero?'

'The Fatherland.'

'Fuck you.'

Montonero pressed the barrel of the Luger up and into Passarella's ribs.

'Don't disrespect an officer of the Navy.'

'What navy?'

'The Argentine Navy, *cabrón*! Our armed forces!'

'What's that got to do with you? You're no soldier.'

'Lieutenant Commander Ricardo Montonero, on secondment to the National Security Services,' corrected Montonero.

'You bastard...' breathed Passarella and Montonero smiled – enjoying the dawning realisation. 'You're the one who ordered Mono's murder!'

'We don't murder anyone. We do the same thing your players do during the game: we correct mistakes, recover passes that have gone astray, discourage empty gestures.'

'You're out of your mind, Montonero ...'

'There's nothing crazy about it. I receive orders and I carry them out. Your players also take orders from you without questioning them ... What would rugby be without discipline? And what would this country have been without us here to clean it up?'

'By murdering kids?'

'Pascua was a lost cause,' said Montonero dismissively. 'A hot-head. Another two or three years and you would have found him throwing his lot in with the *montoneros*, putting bombs on buses.'

'Was it the same with Hernan? Hernan Rocca?'

Montonero looked blank. Then realisation seemed to dawn. 'The scrum-half?' He shrugged, his expression indifferent.

'What do you want?' managed Passarella, his mouth suddenly dry.

'Leave, Passarella. Withdraw your squad from the championship and go travel around Europe before it's too late. Your boys, it's the only way to save their skin.'

Montonero struggled to his feet, attempting to hide the pain shooting through his leg. He cursed Benavides and himself for listening to him and leaving the cane behind.

'I'm not supposed to be here, Passarella. I'm doing this for you, for old times.'

'Which old times?'

Montonero didn't reply. He hobbled away towards the exit.

Passarella sat there, alone and diminished. On the screen, John Wayne was still sitting astride his horse, stiff as a figurine, but Passarella couldn't see him. He had his hands over his face, his palms pressed into his eyes as if trying to squeeze the things he had heard out of his head.

14

They took Mariano the following evening. He was cycling back from training, his holdall slung over his shoulder. A vehicle pulled up alongside him on the Pan-Americana and forced him over towards the pavement. Mariano managed to keep his balance. He put a foot to the ground and turned to curse the idiots responsible, but the doors of the vehicle opened in tandem before he could get the words out.

Two men climbed out, one tall and slightly hunched, the other stubby with a face that promised trouble. They dragged Mariano into the car and sped away. Two old ladies nearby who had stopped to observe the scene hurried silently on their way.

*

The ESMA building was designed as follows: the offices lay on the first floor, with the cells on the floor above; these were little more than a row of alcoves, two metres by one and a half, no toilets and no windows, only a solitary light bulb dangling high enough from the ceiling to avoid giving anyone inside an opportunity to hang themselves with the wiring. These were known as *Capucha*, after the black hoods that were placed over the heads of those who were taken from the cells to their deaths – the less they saw, the less trouble they would cause. They had converted the floor directly beneath the roof into an interrogation room, large enough to torture two people at a time, far enough from the street that nobody would hear the screams of the victims.

Reaching that floor meant going through a back entrance and through a small gate behind the garden that opened directly onto the stairs, meaning that the arrival and departure of prisoners had to be carried out quickly, without a fuss and away from prying eyes.

Mariano was taken straight up to the second floor. Throughout the journey, he and the others had not exchanged a word. The yutas, Montonero's enforcers, had nothing to say to him and Mariano had nothing to ask: the fact they were police officers wanting to make him pay for the meeting with Turco and the others at the tannery was clear.

They flung him into one of the cells. Mariano sat on the floor with his back to the wall and his eyes fixed on the patch of darkness where he knew the door to be. That way, he reasoned, he would at least be able to look them in the eyes when they came to murder him. At some point during the night, he must have dozed off. He awoke to the sound of a latch sliding back – a pool of light flashed briefly across his vision, and then Turco appeared in the doorway. He recognised the two yutas who had snatched him off the street the day before. They pushed his friend in and slammed the cell door shut once more.

Turco landed on Mariano with his fists raised.

'Son of a bitch, did you have to tell them that I was there at the meeting?'

Mariano shoved him backwards into the wall.

'What the fuck are you talking about?'

The venom in Mariano's response said all that was needed.

'It wasn't you?' said Turco, his fists unballing, his aggression seeping away.

'They caught me last night when I was on my way home and brought me here. I don't know anything more than that.'

'Sorry . . .' said Turco.

'Fuck your apology. What do you take me for?'

The door to the cell opened. A new figure appeared framed against the light of the corridor.

'Which one of you is the one they call the Turk?'

*

They took him to the cubbyhole that served as Montonero's office and left him standing in front of the desk without handcuffs.

Turco stood motionless until he heard the sound of approaching footsteps and rusty hinges. He turned: a small man, his uniform creased, a pistol in his belt, the trousers sagging loose and awkward around uneven legs.

'Last Sunday, you were the one who gifted your opponents their second try . . .' Montonero said by way of introduction. He hobbled to his desk and fell into the chair. He fixed his gaze on Turco. 'The centre went left and you followed him like a fool. You left the other guy, the winger, in open space. He would never have scored a try otherwise, even if you'd picked him up and carried him over the line yourself.'

'It wasn't my fault! Santiago was supposed to close the space to the right,' Turco replied before he could stop himself. Then his voice caught and he stared in bewilderment at the strange man masquerading as some kind of soldier. He had no idea who he was, had never seen him before.

'Anyway, they didn't get through that space again,' he muttered sullenly. He would not let a yuta lecture him on how to play rugby.

'You're right, they didn't get through there again,' smiled Montonero, adopting a conciliatory tone. 'That's what makes you a good player. You avoid making the same mistake twice.'

He unbuckled his holster and placed it over the back of his chair. He stared at Turco for a long moment. It felt as though there was nothing else for them to say.

'In here things can also go one of two ways, son.' Montonero rubbed his face. 'If you do the right thing, you win the game. Otherwise, everyone loses because of you.'

'What game? What are you talking about?'

'You've got yourself in trouble. The meeting at the tannery the other night. Did you not hear what they were talking about? Hooligans, communists, degenerates . . .'

'I have nothing to do with them.'

'But you were there. That's enough for me.'

'What do you want from me?'

'I want you to work with us. You just told me yourself that you have nothing to do with those people.'

'I'm not a communist. I'm not anything. What's not clear?'

'Sit down.'

Turco pushed himself into the chair. He felt weak all of a sudden.

'All I need is for you to give me a name every so often,' Montonero went on. 'Those who talk too much, who cause trouble . . .'

'You want me to spy for you?'

'You have to do what your country asks of you.'

'And Mariano?'

'Your friend is a pain in the arse,' shrugged Montonero. 'He plays around with the trade unions, we've had our eye on him for a while. Besides, he's not a good player: he's slow, he thinks too much, he doesn't follow the ball when you have the chance for a counter-attack . . . You're the one I'm interested in. If you collaborate, you live. Otherwise, you die. What's it to be?'

'Get fucked.'

'I didn't realise we were on such impersonal terms.'

'Kindly get fucked.'

Montonero rested the palm of his hand on the desk. He seemed disappointed.

'I only asked for propriety's sake. I knew that would be your answer.'

'Can I go now?'

Montonero smiled encouragingly.

'Let's do it like this. I'll leave the decision up to you. If you prefer, I can put you in the hands of my team on the floor above. They may be able to convince you to change your mind, and one day you might even thank me for saving your skin . . .'

'Or?'

'Or I have you shot immediately, without letting those butchers break your bones first. You don't deserve an end like that, you were a good player.'

Turco felt the bile rising in his throat. He struggled to force it back down.

'I don't want to die. I've not done anything.'

'That's exactly the problem. Everyone in this country has convinced themselves that doing nothing is somehow praiseworthy, to be rewarded. We're at *war*, Turco. You can't just sit on the sidelines and watch.'

'You want to kill me for that? For doing *nothing*? What the fuck?'

'Sooner or later you will have to pick a side. If you refuse to stand with your country now, when I have you by the balls, it means you're already with the other side.'

Montonero steepled his hands, his voice dropping to a soothing murmur. 'Put yourself in my place, Turco. How do I know I can trust you?'

'Then shoot me yourself, you coward! You do it if you think you're able to!'

Montonero looked at him, a veil of disappointment crossing his face. He pulled the pistol out of the holster and tried to get to his feet, but with the weight of the Luger in his hand and without that fucking cane, he was unable to generate enough leverage.

'Help me . . .'

Suddenly overwhelmed and cowed, Turco came closer, caught him under the armpit, and brought him up to his feet.

'Now turn around please . . .'

They stood that way for a few seconds, side by side. Montonero slowly straightening up, regaining his breath, Turco with his eyes fixed on the wall in front.

It was over quickly. Montonero released the safety catch on the Luger, stepped in close to Turco, placed the pistol against his temple and pulled the trigger.

Two of the yutas came running into the room, pistols in hand.

'What happened?'

They looked down and saw Turk's body lying on the floor, his skull cracked open like an egg, grey matter splattered against the wall.

'Go and fetch the other one,' said Montonero, placing his pistol back in its holster. 'And send someone to clean up.'

15

Mariano and Turk were found inside a nondescript vehicle. Trousers around their knees, shirts unbuttoned, each with a bullet hole in the head. Turco was holding a pistol, clutched tightly in his hand.

'Two *maricones*,' the police officer told the assembled journalists. They had been called to the Avenida Costanera, by the 51-kilometre marker. The car had been found in a lay-by overrun with weeds and discarded bottles that was favoured by truck drivers for their illicit rendezvous with local whores.

'And by faggots like these two.' The officer gestured towards the horrific scene inside the car. The bodies were grey, the skin almost like marble. 'Looks like the big one shot the boy and then killed himself.'

'What was the motive?' asked one of the journalists.

'You'd have to ask them,' replied the officer.

'Is it true that they played for La Plata?' asked another.

'Fucked if I know. But if they did, make sure your articles say that deviants like this have no place in sport. Fucking disgusting. Argentina must be kept clean, *puta madre!* Especially with the World Cup coming.'

16

That evening, the boys gathered in the changing room. Their holdalls cast to the ground, zipped up, their eyes bewildered. A few of them had gone to the mortuary to spy on the undertakers as they loaded the wooden caskets into a van and carted them off who knew where. Now they were all left staring into space and waiting for someone else to speak first.

'They weren't gay,' Raúl said. But that wasn't news to anyone. Mariano and his girlfriend – an eighteen-year-old blonde he had met at school – were known to go at it every night. Turco had been married for a brief period, and had later moved in with someone from his hometown who had three children. *Maricones*? Those two?

'Nobody believes that,' said Santiago, 'not even the journalists who wrote it.'

'They were murdered,' said another. 'Just like Mono. It's that simple.'

'Ask yourselves why,' said Passarella gruffly. His face had aged by a decade, the crow's feet like knife cuts at the corners of his eyes.

None of the boys replied.

'Because we challenged their authority, that's why,' he said, his piercing gaze going around their faces one by one. 'Those ten minutes of silence at the ground the other week. You thought they'd let that go?'

'So what do we do?' someone asked.

'We leave this place,' said Passarella.

They looked at him, confused. Leave where? How?

'I called a friend of mine who went off to play in France. He told me they would take us all in. Political asylum.'

'We let them win, boss?' asked Santiago.

Passarella barked a humourless laugh. 'They've already won.'

'Let's take a vote,' offered another voice.

The coach shook his head. 'I've already made my decision. The team is one thing, your life is another. In these circumstances, everybody decides for themselves.'

'No,' said Raúl. 'Mariano and Turco were killed together. We also decide together.'

They took the bucket that held the beers and emptied it. From his holdall, Raúl pulled out Mono's notebook. He ripped out a page and tore it into strips.

'Those who want to stay write "yes". Those who want to leave write "no".'

They passed Jorge's pen around and placed the

pieces of paper in the bucket. Then Gustavo, the youngest member of the team, pulled them out one by one.

Twelve yes, one no.

'That was mine,' said Passarella. He turned and walked out of the changing room without another word.

'What now?' asked Jorge.

'We stay. And we finish the season,' replied Santiago. 'We get one over on those bastards!'

'How exactly do we finish it? We're three starters short . . .'

'I can ask my brother,' said Pablo. 'He's two years younger than me but he knows how to play and he's watched all of our games. He'll pick up our moves.'

'We'll go and pick up the others from the academy. We'll teach them how we play,' said Raúl. The idea was starting to appeal to him.

'Who exactly will teach them? The boss has gone.'

'He'll be back,' said Raúl.

'And if he isn't?'

'I'm telling you, he will.'

*

Raúl went looking for him that night. He went up the stairs at his home and knocked. No reply. He tried the door, which was unlocked. He went in.

He was expecting to find a home that took after Passarella himself, grouchy and off-kilter. Instead, everything inside was in perfect order, carefully curated, symmetrical, minimalist, a scent of cleanliness and polish hanging in the air, no grease stains around the hob of the gas cooker, a few small jars resting on the sill of the solitary window. Raúl looked closer: they were old containers of tomato sauce that Passarella had filled with bulbs, flowers, sweet potato tubers . . . On the wall beside the window were dozens of photographs in black and white, each with a neat wooden frame: Passarella when he was a young boy and still had the use of both legs, his rugby team around him, a menacing scowl as he threw himself into a tackle, the elation after a try, the ball raised high above outstretched arms in the same pose that he, Raúlito, adopted when scoring a try.

'What are you doing here?'

Passarella had returned. He had a large suitcase in his hand. Without waiting for an answer from Raúl, he tossed it open onto the bed and started flinging clothes into it from his wardrobe.

'We have to talk,' said Raúl.

Passarella continued to throw clothes from one to the other. Shirts and trousers, once carefully folded inside the wardrobe, cast into the suitcase like rags.

'Boss . . .'

Now he emptied a shoebox full of ointments onto the bed. Unguents for his leg.

'Are you going to listen to me?'

'No.'

The younger man walked up to his coach and grabbed him by the lapel of his jacket, tried to pin him to the wall. Perhaps Passarella had anticipated it. He managed to free his arm and swung a haymaker into Raúl's stomach, leaving him doubled over.

Passarella left him no time to recover his breath: he pushed him backwards onto the bed and pinned him down with an agility that belied his damaged leg, his age and everything else. He pushed a hand into Raúl's face and squeezed, contorting his grip into something like a mask.

'Don't you dare ever put your hands on me again! Ever!'

He let Raúl go and climbed back to his feet. A moment later he was back to packing as if nothing had happened.

Raúl sat up on the bed, rubbing his chest. 'You're a coward,' he wheezed between coughs.

'I'm someone who wants to live.'

'Mono wanted to live too.'

'Otilio Pascua was a kid who wanted to play at being a revolutionary. The people he was up against don't like playing games.'

'And Turco? And Mariano?'

Passarella turned to face him, resignation stamped across his face.

'It will be a bloodbath, Raúl.'

'We've not done anything.'

'You're twenty years old. They want to kill you because they cannot understand you and trying to drives them to insanity.'

For a moment Raúl felt the temptation to grab his coach again, make him realise that he was capable of smashing his face in because a twenty-year-old could do that too – expose those like Passarella for what they were: old men who had aged without grace, who were broken inside, darkened by a life different to the one they had imagined when they themselves were twenty years old. *It would be no good though*, he thought, *he wouldn't understand. He'll never understand.*

'You go too Raúl, leave this country,' Passarella told him. 'Tell the other boys, you have to accept the invitation.'

'You're past your time, boss. We're staying. You can run.'

He left.

17

Sunday came around. Their game was far from home in a ground packed with spectators. When the players emerged from the changing rooms, a silence fell. Anyone in the crowd who had come expecting scarred faces and fierce scowls was left disappointed: the team from La Plata were little more than a bunch of kids. Slightly skinnier and a week older than before. Nobody found the courage to applaud. Everybody was waiting to see what would happen next.

And it did happen, even without anything having been said as they put the shirts on the three academy kids who had been pushed into combat on the front lines of the first team. It happened after Raúl glanced over to their bench to seek reassurance despite knowing it was empty because the boss had gone and no one had seen him since the afternoon when they had placed their lives into the bucket that usually held the beers and had unanimously decided to stay, even at the risk of losing those lives. It happened when the referee said yes, a minute's silence for the two murdered players from La Plata, two *desgraciados* found with their genitals exposed and holes through their heads. 'But only one minute,' repeated the referee. 'One minute and then we play.'

It happened again. The minute stretched and stretched, a stubborn wait until the silence transformed into something else entirely, life rushing into it and coming out in the sound of boots beating against the turf. It was Santiago who started it. He began to stamp his feet against the dry grass of the pitch, as if he was marching. His teammates began to follow him, then the crowd in the stands rose to their feet, all joining in and pummelling the wooden floorboards in a slow and leaden rhythm – 10,000 people marching on the spot, a brazen challenge that took the silence and turned it into music, every step a forbidden thought, every thud of the feet a final salute to an Argentina that had turned to slaughtering its own children in the street, to spitting out the flesh of its flesh, to playing at life and death in the absurd name of the Fatherland.

*

The following morning Montonero, dressed in his uniform, was in Benavides's office. The colonel appeared ready to exercise judgment.

'Another game like that, with those imbeciles celebrating their dead, and I'm sending you to coach them, Montonero! At the bottom of the ocean!'

'What would you have me do?' asked Montonero.

'Get them all out from under my feet. The World

Cup starts in a month and we can't afford any troublemakers showing us up. Make it so that team never existed. Is that clear?'

Absolutely clear, thought Montonero.

*

At home, Raúl was eating with his head bent low over his plate. Teresa was watching him, her spoon in her hand, the minestrone untouched in front of her.

'You're next. You know that, right?'

No, Raúl did not know that. He had not even stopped to consider whether there would be a next one. The last question he had asked himself had come when he slipped the scrap of paper with 'yes' written on it in block letters, bold and clear so that he would never forget it, into the bucket.

'Your coach is gone. You're the oldest player in the squad, you're the captain . . .'

'So?'

'So you tell me.'

'That's why I have to stay,' Raúl told her. He tried to reach out and stroke her face, but Teresa pulled away. She was angry.

'They offer us a move to France and you say no?'

'I'm happy here.' He sounded unconvinced, but it was too late regardless.

'Here?! What do you mean by here?'

'Here,' he repeated. 'In Argentina.'

'Have you seen what they did to your friends? The only way to survive here is to bury your head in the sand! Do you plan to keep it there for the rest of your life?'

'No . . .'

'So let's move to France, Raúlito.' She tried to soften her tone. 'We will just about be able to pay the rent with the two pesos I've rubbed together from working at the café . . .'

'What's that got to do with it? There's the garage to think about . . .'

Teresa got up from the table, dragging her chair back to maximise the effect.

'That's your toy. Like the motorbike. And the rugby team, the championship and all the rest of it.' She spat out the words. 'You're still a child, Raúl. A spoiled child!'

'What's gotten into you? You were happy when we moved in here.'

'We were many things before, you and I.'

You bitch, thought Raúl.

'I don't want someone waking me up in the middle of the night to tell me that they've fished you out of the river,' Teresa continued. 'I don't want to come and identify you at the morgue.' She seemed sincere. But to Raúl it felt as though she was talking about a different person.

18

In those feverish days, anticipation for the World Cup had begun to build like a huge wave, greatly anticipated by all – the assassins, the commanders, the despairing, the fearful, those who did not understand, those who thought that Argentina was a normal country and that the occasional distressing stories of people being tortured, trussed up and disappearing were just exaggerations and jealous words muttered because all the eyes of the world were being cast their way. *El Mundial* had arrived and brought with it all the great football stars from around the globe, who had landed with their identical blazers and identical ties, their neatly-pressed smiles, to be received at the airport with the full fanfare of the *Junta Militar*: '*Bienvenidos in Argentina, tierra de derechos y de humanos.*' Even the butchers joined in the joke: '*Welcome to Argentina, the land of rights and humanity.*' Any other message was nothing but communist propaganda; the rest were all hippies and degenerates, the rest were not real, the rest did not count, the rest did not exist. And if they did exist, they were to be eliminated.

*

Santiago's number came up next. He was the one who had set off the carnival of stamping feet at the stadium. They went to get him straight from the training ground, down at La Plata. They waited for him to leave, to say goodbye to his teammates. They followed him in a car at walking pace for two blocks, then bundled him in and took him to ESMA.

There he was, Santiago – the Native American.

Under the roof of the Capucha, on the top floor of the School of Mechanics, they had tied him to a metal chair fixed firmly into the ground with four screws. Montonero stood in front of him. He had taken off the jacket of his uniform, loosened the tie. He supervised the preparations, giving brief, matter-of-fact instructions about the electrodes attached to the young man's genitals, the *picana* cattle prod that was to be inserted directly up his rectum. 'Not too far, otherwise he might pass out with the first shock.' Santiago was to be kept awake, butchered but lucid.

Montonero gave a nod, one of his subordinates switched the amplifier on – one of those used for electric guitars but which worked equally well for sending electric currents through the rectum of an agitator. They had picked it up from the home of a student who had been brought in to ESMA: requisitioned for the Fatherland along with the guitar, a bright red Fender Mustang.

The yuta standing by twisted the volume knob a

bit at a time, until Santiago's body stretched out like a violin string.

'More?' he asked. Montonero didn't respond.

'That'll do,' he said after a while.

Santiago flopped back into the chair. The crippled officer moved in closer to the boy, pulled a handkerchief from his pocket, wiped the sweat from his face.

'Someone gave you some bad advice, my boy. You used to be a rugby team, now you've become a handful of degenerates.' He dabbed at a droplet of blood dripping from his nose. 'And by doing so, you've put your title at risk.'

The boy was on the verge of passing out, but he forced himself to focus on that voice, the rambling stream of consciousness.

'We need to save your teammates from your fate, Santiago Sanchez. I need a few names – the loudest troublemakers, the ones who put those half-baked thoughts into your heads. You're fucked anyway, but perhaps it is not too late to save some of them. So?

What do you say?'

Santiago said nothing. His interrogator gave a sign and the voltage resumed. Santiago's torso looked as though it was about to tear in half, then he jolted back into the chair. Montonero came in closer. This time he didn't waste time with the handkerchief.

'I'm going to continue turning the dial back and forth until your balls are fried. What's the decision?' Montonero leaned in with his ear close to the boy's mouth. Santiago's swollen lips started to move, shaping themselves into syllables. Montonero listened attentively. Then he nodded, satisfied.

*

They disposed of Santiago's lifeless body by the landfill near Leon. The eyes swollen shut, mouth full of clotted blood, welts from the straps across the chest and wrists. They didn't even bother staging a show or faking anything. They left him there, murdered. Full stop.

19

Raúl fished Santiago's number seven shirt out of the bag and handed it to a wafer-thin young boy standing next to him.

'Try it on.'

The boy put it on: a bit baggy, but it would do. His name was Alejo, and he had turned fifteen just the month before.

'Raúl, are you sure?' asked Pablo.

'They won't let us play without a full team.'

'I'm talking about the kid. Are you sure we should be taking him onto the pitch with us?'

'There are two games left until the end of the season. You want to quit now?'

They had postponed this moment: it was time to decide what to do. Train, go home, escape.

'They won't be able to kill us all,' offered Gustavo, himself only a year older than the new recruit.

Raúl looked Alejo in the eye. 'What do you want to do?'

The boy returned his gaze. 'In open play, I keep an eye on their stand-off, I tackle anything that comes my way, and I'm in the back row in the scrum. Right?'

The others raised a smile. Raúl ruffled his hair in a show of affection.

'Let's get training,' he said. Nobody protested.

*

They trained with the usual rhythm, all thoughts focused on the game as always, as if the boss was still there with them. Nobody paid any attention to the figure in the white raincoat sitting at the top of the stand.

Montonero, with his collar up to protect against the recent cold turn in the weather, didn't miss a single play. He held a piece of paper in his hand: he observed, jotted something down, then went back to enjoying the training session. Anyone watching him from the pitch might have gained the impression that he was creating set-plays, variations, attacking strategies. In reality, the paper contained the names of the survivors, Raúl and the others. Every so often Montonero would circle one of the names with his pen. There was no rush.

He left before the session was over: it was about to rain and the humidity played havoc with the screws they had shoved into the wounded leg.

*

Montonero walked into the School of Mechanics as

the first fat raindrops began to fall, each the size of a walnut.

He looked out of the window of his office: over towards the ocean, the sky had turned black. It was going to rain all night.

Behind him, the two yutas he had summoned awaited their orders. The tall, stooped one held a pump-action shotgun in his hand: he had looked around for somewhere to place it, then decided to keep hold of it – the conversation with the captain was sure to be short.

Montonero pulled the creased paper out of his pocket and passed it over to the shorter of the two.

'Tonight,' he said simply.

'Are we bringing them here?'

'No need. We're not wasting time.'

'It's going to start raining heavily soon . . .' said the tall one.

'Even better,' said Montonero with a tight, humourless smile. 'There'll be nobody out there in your way.' He looked at them. They were good men. Excellent at breaking bones, at not asking questions, at remaining detached even as they hewed through their prisoners' flesh. The back stories of the people they arrested or killed were of no interest to them. He was jealous: they had the assassin's touch.

'It'll be cold,' he said by way of dismissal. 'Wrap up warm.'

20

Montonero's enforcers climbed onto the bus. One of them approached the driver and pulled one side of his jacket open to reveal a pistol and something that might have been a badge.

'Pull over,' he told him.

The driver glanced down, saw the pistol and brought the bus to a halt.

'End of the line!' his partner called out to the few people scattered on board.

They all began to make their way off without any questions. Shuffling outside, where there was only darkness and rain.

'Not you,' he said to Jorge, pushing him back into his seat with a firm hand on his chest.

The only ones left on the bus now were the boy, the driver and the two yutas. The shorter of the two men placed a hand on the shoulder of the driver, who had stayed firmly in place throughout, his eyes fixed on the road ahead. 'Move. Let's go!'

He closed the doors and shifted the vehicle into gear.

*

Gustavo stopped in front of the door to his house and fumbled for the keys in his pocket. He cursed, his task made harder by the darkness, the rain and the stack of books he had carried all the way down the Avenida de Mayo, as the *colectivos* services no longer ran at those hours. He was doing an accounting course at night school, coming home every day at midnight and collapsing with exhaustion. His father had told him, '*Hijo*, you have to choose, rugby or school.' But how could you choose at that age? Gustavo wanted everything – the evening classes, the championship, his place in the first team, the accounting certificate. Although at that moment he would have settled for his house keys.

'Papers!'

There were two of them. They had appeared from nowhere and were suddenly right up in his face. Parked alongside the pavement, he saw the outline of a black Ford Falcon with the engine running and the doors open.

The one who had spoken to him was shorter than Gustavo by a few inches. He shone a torch into the boy's face.

'Hurry up, *niño*. Your papers?'

Gustavo tried to find his ID card, but the books in his arms restricted his movement.

'Could you hold these for me?'

The man hesitated for a second, then put the torch in his pocket and took the books.

'Hurry up, it's raining . . .' muttered his partner. He had pulled a copy of *Clarín* from his jacket and was holding it over his head to provide some shelter from the rain.

'Shut up!' said the smaller one. He turned to the boy. 'We'll be done here in a moment, right *niño*?'

The boy rummaged in his pocket, found the ID card and handed it over.

'Gustavo Kaminsky.'

'I live here,' replied the boy. 'Can I go now?'

The man tucked the card into his pocket.

'No, Gustavo. You can't.'

The books hit the deck with a loud thump and they grabbed him by the armpits and shoved him into the Falcon. He tried to say something, but one of his assailants had his fingers pressed into his throat and was cutting off his breathing. *But my books . . .* he thought as the car pulled away.

His books were scattered on the ground, pages strewn open, the paper gradually soaking through with the rain.

At that time of morning, the squealing of the car's brakes was heard by everyone. In that corner of the Almafuerte barrio, the houses were tall and packed in closely, as if clamouring for the best view of the traffic along the distant Pan-Americana. Thin walls, plywood shutters, toilets at the end of a hallway. Inside, families who had gravitated to Buenos Aires from the surrounding countryside struggled through their daily lives.

The two enforcers were in a hurry, their clothes crumpled from their nightly excursions. They headed straight for the front door and burst through it with a kick. They knew where to look.

Pablo, dressed in a string vest, saw them coming from the window: he saw the Falcon, he saw the yutas. He knew he was in trouble. He put on his shoes and sprinted out. His mother made no effort to stop him: she looked on as he climbed the stairs, watching as two men with their jackets flapping behind them followed him up them three at a time. One of them held a gun in his hand, squat and blunt as a broom. She brought a hand to her mouth and chewed on a fingernail until it drew blood. She was thinking how stupid she had been to have only one child.

Two floors further up, Pablo realised that this route offered no escape – that it offered nothing at all: he had reached the top – the stairs ended at the rooftop. He stopped, and from behind him he could hear his assailants' footsteps as they came closer.

They emerged wheezing onto the rooftop. Pablo was waiting for them a metre from the cornice. He raised a closed fist in the air.

'Stop!' called out the one holding the gun.

The boy shook his head, glanced out over the edge and pitched himself over, arms outstretched in front as if targeting an opponent's legs.

There was a thud from the street below. Then nothing.

21

That evening, the survivors gathered in a small bar in La Boca facing out over the river. They knew that Pablo had killed himself and that the other two, Gustavo and Jorge, were at that moment being held captive and likely being tortured to death.

'We don't go back to the pitch,' said Raúl. Around him were gathered a few of the academy boys and the remains of the first team. 'If we keep training, we'll all be dead within three days.'

'So what do we do?'

'We do nothing. We wait for Sunday . . .' – he opened

the bag he had placed under the table – '. . . and we play our last game.'

He pulled out three shirts.

'Lucio, you're going out on the wing . . . Miguelito and Fernando, you're replacing Jorge and Gustavo in the second row . . .' The boys took the shirts from him. The oldest of them was sixteen.

'Any questions?' Nobody spoke. Nobody moved.

'Then we'll meet up on Sunday,' said Raúl.

'Where are you going in the meantime?'

'Home. If they want to find me, they'll find me anywhere.'

*

Outside the rain had stopped. A northerly breeze had come in that slashed the face like broken glass. It had gone on the offensive for 3,000 kilometres, sweeping across rural landscapes of low skies, swollen with cold Patagonian air that it carried all the way to the outskirts of Buenos Aires. Maybe Teresa would like to move down there, to seek a last sliver of land where the two oceans met. Who would possibly think to go looking for them at the end of the world?

He heard heavy footsteps behind him. A hand brushed against him.

'You're the only one left, Raúlito . . .'

He turned around sharply. It was Passarella. He seemed thinner, older and more fragile than before.

'Boss! Shit, you nearly killed me . . .'

'You were lost in your thoughts. You didn't hear me coming.'

'When did you get back?'

'I never left. I haven't moved from my house.' He pointed to a nearby bar. 'Want to get a beer?'

*

The waiter placed the beers on an unsteady marble table.

'It has one leg shorter than the others,' Passarella nodded towards the table.

The waiter bent over to slide a piece of cardboard under the offending leg. He tested it. He stood up, satisfied. 'That's an easy problem to fix.'

Passarella waited for him to move out of earshot.

'In Argentina, everyone has become like that guy. They play at who can be the biggest asshole.'

He took a sip of his beer. He seemed unsure where to begin. Then he made his mind up.

'So, you're playing on Sunday.'

'Yes, we're playing.'

Passarella took a long swig with his eyes closed: he looked thirsty. He put the glass down.

'I'll be there too.'

Raúl had not been expecting that. He had been steeling himself for an argument, but now that the boss was taking his side, he no longer knew what to say. The clouds of fear rose up through his chest, the disruptive questions he would have kept to himself, like dogs on a leash.

'And what do we do after that?'

'We go to France.'

'We could have done that before. We've lost three more since.'

'We'll go as men, Raúl. We'll have finished the season. This time we won't be running away.'

'You sure about that, boss?'

'I'm not sure about anything anymore . . .' Passarella looked at Raúl. 'Actually, that one of us has to stay alive. That I'm sure about.'

'Why?'

'Because one of us will have to tell the story . . .'

He raised his near-empty glass. They drained their beers by way of a toast.

'I'll give you a ride home.'

'You know that I refuse to climb on that death-trap. I'll see you on Sunday, Raúlito.'

Of course, thought Raúl. *Hopefully.*

22

Passarella opened the door to his home and immediately froze: in front of him stood Montonero. On his feet, no uniform, scrawny shoulders hunched over. He continued to examine the old photographs on the wall, as if he had not heard Passarella's arrival.

'What are you doing in my house?' asked Passarella. A pair of hands grabbed at him and pulled him in, and the boss realised how ridiculous the question was: what did he think Montonero was doing in here? He had come to kill him, what else would it have been?

'Do you remember the days when I used to referee?' Montonero asked without turning to face him.

'I remember you fixing matches,' replied Passarella. He hoped it would all be over quickly. He was not prepared for it to end with him wetting himself in fear in front of these people.

'They all used to take the piss . . .' Montonero seemed immersed in the photographs. As if he had completely forgotten about Passarella. '"Look at his little mouth," they used to say, "shaped like a little heart, like he's puckering up for the camera . . . and those eyes, slanted and half-shut . . . he always looks so sad, that kid, he thinks too much. How will he ever become a man?"'

He turned around. Without the disguise afforded to him by his uniform, Montonero was nothing more than a scrawny little man. Insignificant.

'And then I enlisted. And they stopped giving me shit. I made my way up the ladder without ever firing a shot.'

'They have you doing their dirty work for them, don't they?'

Montonero came in close to Passarella. Seeing the two of them together was like seeing two old trees in the forest, each contorted, leaning on damaged legs, heads inclined slightly to counterbalance the weight of their torso. For the first time, Passarella regretted not walking with a cane: at the very least he could have smashed this half-wit in the face before his attack dogs killed him.

'We've done a good job,' said Montonero softly. 'Anarchists, vagrants, trade unionists, revolutionaries. Now it's the turn of the undecided. People like you, Passarella. Why did you come back?'

'To coach my boys.'

'We've already dealt with your boys, all of them,' Montonero replied dispassionately.

Passarella went for him, but the enforcers stepped in before he could strike a blow.

'You're out of your mind!' he yelled.

'And you're a fool. You never saw what this country was becoming before we arrived. Workers on strike, university occupations, terrorists wandering around freely . . . What were we supposed to do? Turn the other cheek while they destroyed Argentina?'

'What do you want from me?'

'I'm trying to save your skin. You're a good coach and you're a cripple like me . . . I'll tell you what we'll do – I'll put a new passport in your pocket, put you on an aeroplane and you can go fuck around somewhere else.'

'I'm going nowhere, asshole.'

Montonero didn't reply. He turned around, hobbled over to the switches on the wall, flicked the lights of the house off one by one, closed the lone window in the room. Then he walked back over to Passarella. He stood in front of him and shone a torch into his face.

'And I'm telling you that by the end of the night, you will have changed your mind.'

The torch went out.

23

Raúl glanced over at the clock on the wall. Passarella had not arrived and the game was due to start in five minutes. He looked at his teammates sitting on the benches of the changing room, all the academy kids he had brought into the first team. They were ready. Waiting only for him.

'Let's go,' he said.

The small stadium in La Plata was packed like Raúl had never seen it before. And never before could he recall seeing it so absorbed, in such electric suspense. He looked up at the stands, unaware that Teresa was standing among the masses. She had not told him that she was coming because certain things were better left unsaid and purely done; after all, it was only a game of rugby and nobody could possibly be hurt in a game of rugby. That was the only reason she was there – to watch Raúl play, to follow him across the pitch at every moment, keep him within her sight until the final whistle, at which point she would run to pick him up from the changing rooms and take him away as he stood, covered in mud and full of conflicting emotions. She would take him away from that pitch and that city for good, because what Raúl did not know was that she had sold the few pieces of jewellery she had and bought two tickets for a coach headed south for three nights and three days all the way to Punta Arenas, three nights and three days across the relentless plains when they would find time to rectify the ill-spoken words of those past months. All that mattered was that the game would be behind them, that Argentina would be behind them, along with all those who had been bewitched into looking away while the country fell apart. Everything would be behind them and there would finally be relief for her and for Raúl. *Just let it be so, oh Lord, please, oh Lord, please let it be so . . .*

There were many things Raúl did not know on that day – about Teresa and Punta Arenas, about where life would take him after that game, about whether it really was the right decision to have yourself murdered out of stubbornness, over a stupid principle. Nor did he know that, at that moment, Passarella was hanging from a butcher's hook on the ceiling of the Capucha, that the butchers themselves were standing back from as piss dripped on the floor and blood and life leaked from the gaping wound in his stomach, watching with disdain as the dark puddle grew beneath the dying man while they smoked and thought about how they would have to clean up afterwards. If it had been left up to them, he would have been thrown out of an aeroplane, pushed to his death by the point of a bayonet; but no, Montonero had felt a personal affection for him, and Christ what a personal affection. 'Hang him up,' he had said, 'and let me know how long it takes him to die.' So they had obeyed and now they watched as the cripple bled out.

'Our job really is shit,' said the tall one.

'Absolute shit,' agreed his stocky partner.

'But someone has to do it. And it's better to be on the side of those who put people on the hooks.'

'Better to clean up the blood and piss than to be up there ourselves. Crucified without ever knowing why.'

The only ones who knew why were Benavides and Montonero: who had to die and why, how they were to suffer . . . But at that moment the two men were up in the stands at La Plata waiting for the game and the celebration. The colonel nodded towards a box at the top of the stairs, there was a whine of feedback from the speakers and then a marching tune broke out, the kind played at military parades. Montonero began to stamp the foot of his good leg in time with the beat, but immediately stopped because none of the other spectators joined in the festivity. Nobody sang, nobody so much as swayed on the spot as the loudspeakers continued to release the flood of upbeat notes and drum-rolls. Colonel Benavides looked around: the stadium appeared lifeless. He made an angry gesture towards the box, and the music came to an immediate stop.

And the game got underway.

*

Afterwards, people spoke of a clash that was beautiful and futile in equal measure: La Plata chased the ball in vain like a herd of frenzied teenagers and their rivals reluctantly overpowered them, dispirited by the muted and shackled crowd.

Until a minute from the end, when the visitors scored another try, leaving only a conversion to wrap up the game. Two points here or there were of no use to either side, La Plata were long since out of the game, down by forty points.

Raúl handed the ball over to the opposing captain. They exchanged the briefest of glances, but something passed between them in their reflected expressions, something was said without being spoken, perhaps nothing more than a sense of embarrassment, a momentary pain, the weariness of being there.

Whatever it was, those who saw it spoke of how the rival captain, a boy with red hair who was not even in his twenties yet, placed the ball on the ground and started his kicking routine, counting seven steps backwards for the run-up. There he froze. The referee whistled to hurry him along, but still he stood. He looked around, looking to his teammates, then to the players from La Plata.

Another blast of the whistle – more insistent this time – the boy took one last look towards the stands, then began his run-up, but as he took his last step, his body twisted as if trying to escape and he struck the ball at an angle, a thump that sought not the posts but the sky, and below it the stands, the stands where Montonero and Benavides stood and watched the ball fall towards them.

The referee gave a shrill blast to end the game, but the ground, which had been muted until that moment, suddenly exploded into life. The crowd climbed to their feet as one, faces twisted in animation, and turned towards the two figures in uniform, who were looking around, lost and unable to read the moment. From somewhere in the crowd, a voice began to sing the Argentine anthem, 'Hear, mortals, the sacred cry . . . Freedom, freedom, freedom . . . Hear the sound of broken chains . . .' Within seconds, everyone around picked it up in a chorus that swept around the stadium – even

Colonel Benavides rose to his feet for the anthem of the Fatherland, as did the cripple, Montonero, the players on the pitch, Raúl and his boys, all sang in one voice. Victims and butchers, an imitation of brotherhood, united for the last time, yet long-since irreconcilable.

Slowly, Benavides realised that the verses being belted out at the top of their lungs had become something else – venom being spat directly at him, at his uniform, at his generals. He turned swiftly on his heel, hurrying away like a criminal from the scene of the crime, puffed up like a turkey and as cowardly as an assassin. And with him went Lieutenant Commander Montonero, who for a brief moment perhaps found himself thinking about all those who had died over the recent weeks and the thought that they would be waiting for him somewhere, that sooner or later they would meet again, as arrogant and rough around the edges as the way they had played, as he was never able to play.

The last view Montonero saw was that of Raúl, standing in the middle of the pitch, crying and singing and laughing because Argentina had died, his friends had died, his twenty-year-old self had died. And yet something remained, something lived on. Something that had not been broken. Not yet.

Perhaps never.

EPILOGUE

In 1982, devastated by defeat in the Falklands War, the military junta that had come to power via a coup was forced to resign.

In 1996, the 'Nunca Más' ('Never Again') report published by the National Commission on the Disappearance of Persons concluded that the victims of the military regime – those murdered or disappeared and never found – numbered in excess of 30,000.

In April 2012, thirteen officials from the ESMA detention centre were sentenced to life in prison for crimes against humanity. Of the 5,000 detainees who passed through the cells of the School of Naval Mechanics, ninety per cent were murdered.

Raúl Barandiarán is the sole survivor from La Plata's original 1st XV. In total, twenty players from the club were murdered by the regime over the course of four devastating years.

It took twenty years after the killings for La Plata to recover its status as a champion side.

The 1978 World Cup, the jewel in the crown of the junta's propaganda machine, was won by the hosts.

AUTHOR'S NOTE

The first time I visited Argentina, almost thirty years ago, the memories of many of the horrors committed by President Videla's military junta were still intact.

The journey felt like a necessary one, educational: it taught me that no place is the centre of the world. I had come from southern Italy, where another war with another enemy that took no prisoners had taken away my father, among many others. They died in Argentina as in Sicily: the silencing of those who spoke out. In Buenos Aires as in Catania, thinking differently and speaking out against the status quo was seen as an unforgivable sin.

Over the years, I learned to tell the stories of the dead through the words of the living (the Mothers of the Plaza de Mayo, the widows of the Via d'Amelio bombing), I tried to imagine how they had lived and why they had made the decisions they made. It did not console me, but instead led me to understand that it was not fate that lay behind the violence, but rather a twisted mentality, the dark and bleak sensation of power, the greed and thirst of a few, their desire for impunity. In this, President Jorge Videla and Benedetto Santapaola – the mafia boss convicted of the murder of my father among numerous other crimes – bear similarities. Their victims likewise shared similar profiles.

The story of the rugby team from La Plata found its way to me many years later, almost by chance. During one of my travels to Argentina, I read the articles of the great journalist, Gustavo Veiga, who had located the last survivor of that team. Being the last, overcoming evil, is always an unbearable weight, a scar that cannot be seen yet festers within like an ulcer. It happened to those who survived the Holocaust, and it happened to those who survived the round-ups and slaughters in Argentina. That is why the story of that rugby team, wiped out at the spiteful whim of military officers, remained untold, hidden away, protected for so long. It is to the credit of Gustavo Veiga that it came to light. That was when I began to look into it myself, to slowly piece together places and memories.

And from it came this book, which does not seek to simply relay the facts: I preferred instead to imagine the thoughts and actions of those boys who elected to stay and to die. I sought to connect invisible threads that bind together lives that are seemingly distant one from the other: the young officers accompanying anti-mafia magistrate, Paolo Borsellino, who opted to forgo their holidays in order to protect their judge; the young players from La Plata who refused to take refuge in France and opted instead to play their season to its conclusion. I wanted to record more than just their names and the tragedy of their deaths. Because in the end, it matters little whether those boys were Argentine or Sicilian. What matters is how they lived. And how they stood up and said 'no'.

Claudio Fava